THE COSMIC OCTAVE

ORIGIN OF HARMONY
PLANETS – TONES – COLORS
THE POWER OF INHERENT VIBRATIONS

BY

COUSTO

LIFERHYTHM
PUBLICATION

Producted in the LifeRhythm Energy Field:
  Type Layout and Design: Mischka Gerken
  Cover Design: Siegmar Gerken, with Fred Hagenader at Dragon Design
  Editor: Siegmar Gerken
  Proofreader: Elinor Lindheimer
  Coordinators: Dixie Black Shipp and Debra Dizin

Library of Congress Cataloging-in-Publication Data

Cousto.
    The cosmic octave.
    [Oktave. English]
    The cosmic octave : origin of harmony : planets, tones, colors : the power of
inherent vibrations / by Cousto.--[Rev. ed.]
    144 p. cm.
    Includes bibliographic references
    ISBN 0-940795-20-5 (pbk. : alk. paper)
    1. Planets--Miscellanea. 2. Harmonics (Music)--Miscellanea.
    I. Title

BF 1999.C72513   2000
133--dc21   00-034920

Copyright: ©LifeRhythm, Revised Edition, 2000
              ©LifeRhythm, 1988
              P.O. Box 806
              Mendocino CA 95460 USA
              Tel: (707 937-1825 Fax: (707) 937-3052
              Books@LifeRhythm.com   www.LifeRhythm.com

German Edition: ©Simon & Leutner, Germany, 1987
Translated from the German by Christopher Baker and Judith Harrison

Printed in the United States of America

CONTENTS

—— ON THE SUBJECT OF THIS BOOK: ——

"Whoever educates the people without uniting them in a loving way of mind is like someone who weeds without wanting to harvest. Whoever unites the people through a loving way of mind without calming them with music is like someone who harvests without wanting to eat. Whoever calms the people with music but does not perfect them in harmony with the law of nature is like someone who eats but does not thrive."

Da Dai Li Gi
The Book Of Customs [1]

PREFACE

This book deals with the subject of the octave, an integral aspect of the law of harmony, in a manner that will be readily understood by the layman. Here he will discover ways of employing cosmic tones for his benefit and find instructions on how to put planetary tuning forks to use. Since this book is intended for readers with no special knowledge of physics or music theory, those interested in the scientific foundation and theoretical background of this subject are referred to the scientific appendix in this book, which deals with these aspects in greater detail.

One of the central aims of my research has been with the fundamental tone, according to which the instruments of an orchestra are keyed. This tone is also known as the "concert pitch." In this day and age, use is generally made of "A," which vibrates 440 times a second (440 hertz), and which was decided at the 1939 standard pitch conference in London. However, use of this pitch, now used throughout the West, is the result of an arbitrary decision and is not in harmony with the concert pitches used in India and China. The pitches employed in these countries are the fundamental tones that tune every kind of truly cosmic music, quite in keeping with the Confucian teachings of Ancient China.

I do not belong to any particular school of thought, but simply pay attention to what I see around me in nature. My view of the world is not the result of having read particular books but, quite literally, of having "viewed" the "world," and the conclusions and implementations of my work are based on this way of seeing things. Of course, having studied mathematics for many years proved to be very useful, but becoming aware of a truth has very little to do with studying. It is something that simply "happens." It is as if you suddenly tune into a given "wavelength."

"Music is the harmony of Heaven and Earth. Customs form the various stages of Heaven and Earth. All things are transformed by harmony and all things are differentiated by their various stages. The creative origin of music is in Heaven and the customs are formed in accordance with the Earth. When forms become too numerous, confusion occurs. When there is too much creativity, violence occurs. Only when one becomes aware of Heaven and Earth will customs and music come to fruition."[2]

It was the result of a way of seeing things that moved me to combine the old teachings of harmonics with new findings in physics and other sciences. The result is an all-encompassing system of measurement by which it is possible to transpose the movements of the planets into audible rhythms and sounds, and into color. This basic system of measurement clearly demonstrates the harmonic relationship that exists between different kinds of natural phenomena in the fields of astronomy, meteorology and microbiology. In this book, the reader will not only find an explanation of this system of measurement, which, like the harmony of music, is inherent in the general structure of all being, but also be provided with instruction on how to prove these universal relationships. In this way, the contents of this book are not merely understood by the intellect, but can also be experienced in the form of meditation, artistic creativity and erotic ecstasy, whatever the reader's inclination or choice.

The path described here is the path of the glass bead game player, combining as it does "three principles: science, veneration of the beautiful, and meditation. Therefore, a proper Glass Bead Game player should be drenched in cheerfulness like a ripe fruit drenched in its sweet juices. Above all, he should possess the cheerfulness of music, for music is nothing if not an act of courage, a serene, smiling, striding forward and dancing through the terrors and flames of the world."[3]

"The rainbow is the sign of the bond," said God to Noah when the Flood began to subside and rays of sunlight shone on the earth again for the first time after 40 days of rain, with millions of raindrops breaking the sunlight into a colossal rainbow. Scientists have discovered that the rainbow contains information about practically the total structure of matter known today. We owe this knowledge to the physicist, optician and astronomer Josef von Frauenhofer, who discovered that the spectrum of the rainbow contains thin, black lines (know as Frauenhofer lines). These lines provide us with information about the elements a ray of light has passed through before reaching a prism and fanning out into a spectrum. In this way it is possible to discover the entire structure of individual atoms. We experience color and sounds due to our ability to differentiate between varying wavelengths and frequencies. With the help of "the law of the octave," tones can be correlated to certain colors, and vice versa.

As already mentioned, an appendix has been included at the end of this book in order to provide the interested reader with more information on the scientific data and theories on which the subject is based. Appendix A consists of the text of my book *Relating Sound to Color and the Cosmic Octave*,[4] which I published in English and German in Munich in 1990, and which is the basis of both this book and *Die Kosmische Oktave - Der Weg zum Universellen Einklang*,[5] published in 1984 by Synthesis Verlag of Essen, Germany. Appendix A contains an explanation of all the equations necessary for calculating planetary dates into tones and colors, as well as a discussion of the tones of an earth day, earth year and Platonic year, and the tones of the moon and the planets.

The tone of the sun remained unknown until 1981, the year I discovered it, and was first discussed in the brochure *Farbton - Tonfarbe und die Kosmische Oktave,* Vol. II,[6] published in Mainz, Germany in 1982. A chapter of this book titled "The Tone of the Sun" has since been included in *Die Kosmische Oktave, Der Weg zum Universellen Einklang.*

Appendix B consists of two chapters taken from the scientific appendix of the above mentioned book, namely "Kepler's Third Law and Gravitation" and "The Gravitational Length of the Sun." In this way, the scope of the book has been widened to include both theory, albeit in condensed form, and practice; and I now wish the reader much pleasure in getting to know the primordial tones of our World.

CHAPTER 1
PERCEPTION – A FORM OF RESONANCE

Imagine you are in a discotheque. First of all you say hello to some friends and then you order a drink before turning your attention to the light show that transforms the black dance floor into a strange yet familiar world. Above the throbbing beat, a conversation starts up about mantras and different forms of worship. This is reality for life-affirming and dynamic young people at the end of the second millennium. Instead of the prayer-wheel, we now have CD players. Instead of temples, we have discos. Instead of priests, we have rock stars. For a few New Age softies and others who prefer to live in the past of "being here now," these remarks will seem blasphemous but for me and most of my friends, that's the way it is.

To return to the disco, imagine that the disc jockey puts on a song. You hear the words, "Let's dance," and you start moving to the beat. The music is pulling you onto the dance floor, into an energy field beyond thought or logic. You dance until the sweat pours off you; you dance until you are in a state of ecstasy.

"When customs work from the outside to the inside in this way, they have to be complemented by a means of education, which works from the inside to the outside. This is music. The significance Confucian thought assigns to music is to be understood in this way. However, music in the Confucian sense does not only imply the making of certain sounds, it also includes the texts of the songs themselves, the meaningful use of rhythmic movement in holy dances and the general mood generated on these occasions. Music which reflects a harmonious sense of joyousness in an aesthetic and balanced way, which provides boisterous feeling with an ordered and adequate outlet, is the second Confucian means of education. Seen in this way, all feelings that express beauty are music, both in public and private life. Music is art, as customs are science, neither of them separated or abstract commodities but harmoniously united, like the elements of Logos and Eros.[1] This is the philosophy expressed by Dai the Elder and Dai the Younger in *The Book of Customs*, one of the most valuable works in Chinese philosophical literature. Indeed, in the old Chinese wisdom teachings, based on Taoism and expressing Confucianism, music was one of the basic means of improving and refining human life.

This now leads us to another aspect of music, to the process of hearing. This process is not an isolated phenomenon involving only the ears. It entails the whole body. Everybody knows the feeling that runs down your spine when someone scratches fingernails on a hard surface: you have to shudder. Music can also affect you like this through and through. Indeed, happy are those who hear the chords of joy and ecstasy. Happy are those familiar with the tones of our planet. Happy are those who let these tones resound within, attuning themselves to the basic motion and rhythm of our earth.

Perception is the result of resonance, for when we hear or see something, the entire body resounds in unity. In the process of hearing, for example, a sound reaching the outer ear is conveyed into a funnel-shaped passage and compressed, and this is amplified in the tapered shape of the auditory canal. At the far end of the auditory canal, the sound waves reach the eardrum, causing it to vibrate rhythmically. This rhythm is conveyed to the three ossicles in the middle ear, known as the hammer, anvil and stirrup, by the membrane of the eardrum. The three ossicles function like a system of levers, and double and treble the pressure of the sound waves. These sound waves then arrive at a little oval window, which is about 25 times smaller than the eardrum, and which has the effect of increasing the pressure of the sound waves another twenty to thirty times. In this way, the sound pressure is increased by about 150 to 200 times during its journey to the inner ear. The inner ear consists of the cochlea and the semicircular canal. The organ that transforms sound into neural signals is the so-called organ of Corti.

The Corti organ is situated on the basilary membrane in the cochlea and looks like a harp. Sound waves make thousands of small and very thin hairs, known as the cilia, vibrate, whereby the differing length of these hairs is responsible for the reaction to specific frequencies. This means that the sound pattern is divided up according to the pitches involved; i.e., the frequencies are physically separated, depending on the hair cells stimulated. Thus, a piece of music is first amplified in the ear and then played again by the Corti organ. The oscillations of the cilia are scanned by nerve cells and conveyed via neurons to the cerebral cortex. In this way, everything we hear vibrates in our head and resounds in our ears again in the form of sound before being transformed into electromagnetic impulses which are conveyed to the processing centers in the brain. We reverberate with every sound we hear. According to the pitch involved, each vibration will have a certain effect, either stimulating or soothing. Even the intervals in a piece of music can affect us in a certain way.

In the same way, vision is also a manifestation of resonance. As in the case of the ears, signals that are "perceived" by the eyes undergo physical processing before being transformed into electronic signals that are sent to the brain. Both the perception of color and the hearing of sound are determined by the ability of the eyes and ears to distinguish between different frequencies. The color orange-red, for example, has a frequency which is considerably lower than that of blue, while a G of 194.18 hertz (or vibrations per second) is lower than a D of 290.94 hertz. Unlike the ear, which can distinguish between tones spanning about 10 octaves, the human eye can only recognize a range of about one octave. The lowest frequencies that the eye will react to lie in the region of 375 trillion hertz (375,000,000,000,000 hertz), which corresponds to the color red, while the highest frequencies lie in the 750 trillion hertz range, which corresponds to the color blue. All the

purple-red	F	yellow-green	B flat
red	F sharp	green	C
orange-red	G	turquoise	C sharp
orange	G sharp	dark blue	D
yellow-orange	A	prussian blue	D sharp
yellow	B	violet	E

other colors have frequencies lying between these two extremes. By applying the law of the octave, each color can be correlated to a respective tone (see the chart on page 14.)

Both the eye and the ear can differentiate between frequencies (the form of color and pitch, respectively) and intensity (in the form of volume and brightness). However, the eyes have two different ways of perceiving color and intensity.

The cornea acts as a convex lens that conveys rays of light to the inner part of the eye. The lens is made up of layers of differing refracting powers and is contained within a transparent, elastic membrane. It controls focal length, and thus the strength of the image projected onto the retina, the actual organ of sight. The retina transforms the images projected onto it into neural impulses that are transmitted to the brain in coded form. The retina has light-sensitive receptors, which are not all activated at the same time. The so-called retinal cones, which consist of three kinds of cones of differing spectral sensitivity, are responsible for the differentiation of frequencies for the perception of color. In contrast, there are spindle-shaped rods that are sensitive to nuances in the range of black and white light and that are mainly put to use in dim conditions and at night.

Visual acuity is determined by the density of the optical cells in the retina. Human beings have over 250 million (250,000,000) optical cells, each eye having 125 million. Six to seven million of these are the cones responsible for the perception of color, while 120 million are the rods responsible for black and white vision. In the middle of the retina, where the resolving power is strongest, the human eye has more than 150 thousand optical cells per square millimeter. The rods contain a retinal pigment, known as visual purple or rhodopsin. This pigment consists of the protein opsin and a chemical substance very similar to carotene. Under the influence of light, rhodopsin is broken down into its component parts, while exposure to darkness regenerates it. During the latter process, vitamin A (carotene) is taken from the blood, which explains why lack of vitamin A not only leads to night-blindness, but also affects vision in dim conditions.

There are three different kinds of rod cells responsible for the perception of color. These differ according to the retinal pigments involved, having either green, blue or yellow receptors. These colors are the basic vibrations of our visual pigments; in other words, each individual color can be perceived by one single receptor. It is of interest to note that perception of red, for example, is induced by two retinal pigments or rod cells, namely those having receptors for blue and for yellow pigments. It has been observed that certain frequencies of the color spectrum make certain receptors resonate. According to the frequency involved (or spectral color), only one, two or three different kinds of receptors will be activated. The perception of color is first determined by the three different kinds of receptors that transform physical impulses into input codes for the data processing system of the nerves and the brain. When the eye perceives color, a color value is broken down into three components by the receptors and then added back together again, enabling us to perceive the original value.

As you can see, sight is more complex than hearing. Indeed, the more you know about the processes of human sensory perception, the more respect you will have for your body and the way it functions. Seeing things from a biological point of view is also a means of increasing consciousness. The more you know about the way your senses function, the better you put shapes, colors and sound to use for your inner development. On a logical, (bio-logical) level, old magic rites will suddenly start to make sense and can be carried out with a new and more subtle consciousness. The alchemist teaching that the microcosm is a mirror of the macrocosm entails a very scientific concept, namely that vibrations that come from without continue to resound within. It is only in this way that we are able to perceive anything at all. In a physical sense, there is no such thing as color. Instead, there are only combinations of waves perceived as color, depending on the wave lengths and frequencies involved, as well as subjective factors. The same applies to sound. Bats can hear frequencies up to 100,000 hertz that are much too high for the human ear. Thus, there is no such thing as sound either. There are only frequencies. We can "hear" some of them because our ears have the ability to resonate to the range of the frequency involved. Multi-media art is a means of deliberately producing resonance in certain ranges of frequency in order to generate certain reactions. This is how music and light shows cause a release of physical energy. The more you are able to let this energy flow freely, the more your whole body will be able to resonate in reaction and the closer you will come to that state known as ecstasy.

CHAPTER 2
THE LAW OF THE OCTAVE

In this chapter I would like to examine the phenomena that determine the color, or timbre, of a tone in greater depth. The explanation of these phenomena is to be found in the overtone series. The most important overtone is the octave tone, which is to be the main subject of discussion in this chapter. However, the scope of this book does not allow me to go into great depth on this subject and those who wish to know more are referred to the scientific appendix at the end of this book.

If you pluck a string on a guitar or sitar, you will not only hear the fundamental tone but also a whole series of other tones, which are whole-number multiples of this basic frequency. Timbre is the sum of the fundamental tone and the overtones, which together are also known as a partial tone series. Since the fundamental tone is the first partial tone, the first overtone (octave tone) is the second partial tone. The second overtone, the fifth in the first octave, also known as the 12th, is the third partial tone, Papers on music theory are mainly concerned with partial tones. The number of the partial tone discloses the relationship of the frequency to the fundamental tone. Thus the second partial tone (octave tone) has exactly double the frequency of the fundamental tone, while the third partial tone (or twelfth) has three times the frequency, and so on.

The intervals are determined by the ratio of the partial tones. The simpler the integral ratio, the purer the interval will be. On the other hand, the farther apart the numerical values of a partial tone ratio are, the more dramatic or disharmonious the impression will be. The overtone series and its structure contain many secrets. The whole basis of the science of harmony derives from the ratios of the overtones to each other. Indeed, music and mathematics are very closely related.

The following table shows the overtone series, starting with the

fundamental tone of C at 64 hertz, as well as the interval factors and
the real frequencies of the individual overtones:

OVERTONE	PARTIAL TONE	FACTOR	FREQUENCY	INTERVAL	OCTAVE
Fundamental	1.	1	64	Prime	Fundamental octave tone
1.	2.	2	128	Octave	1st octave
2.	3.	3	192	Fifth	1st octave
3.	4.	4	256	Octave	2nd octave
4.	5.	5	320	Major Third	2nd octave
5.	6.	6	384	Fifth	2nd octave
6.	7.	7	448	Natural Seventh	2nd octave
7.	8.	8	512	Octave	3rd octave
8.	9.	9	576	Major Whole tone	3rd octave
9.	10.	10	640	Major Third	3rd octave
10.	11.	11	704	–	3rd octave
11.	12.	12	768	Fifth	3rd octave
12.	13.	13	832	–	3rd octave
13.	14.	14	896	–	3rd octave
14.	15.	15	960	Major Seventh	3rd octave
15.	16.	16	1024	Octave	4th octave

Anyone who is not a musician will probably not know what to
make of terms such as "fifth" or "major third," but that is of no
conequence here, since our main area of interest is the phenomenon of
the octave. The striking fact is that there is only one partial tone in the
fundamental octave, while in the next higher octave there are two,
with four in the second, and eight in the third. Were the table to be
extended, there would be sixteen partial tones in the fourth higher
octave, 32 in the fifth, 64 in the sixth, and so on.

In other words, in this table the difference in the frequency from
one partial tone to another consists of a constant 64 hertz. From octave to octave this difference in frequency is doubled, so that there are
64 hertz from the first octave to the second, 256 hertz from the third
to the fourth, and 512 hertz from the fourth to the fifth.

In order to explain this more clearly, several illustrations are included. I recommend that you take a good look at them and, if you
need to make a table of your own with another fundamental frequency
like the one above.

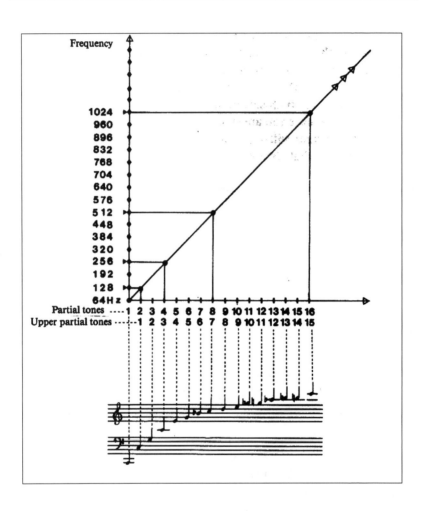

Figure 1. **Overtones**

The diagram demonstrates the relationship of the overtone (or upper partial tone) series to the corresponding frequencies. The horizontal coordinate contains the first 16 partial tones, while the vertical one shows the frequencies involved. As the graph demonstrates, the ratio is a linear function.

Note: To octavate or transpose by octaves means to double a given frequency (in order to reach the next higher octave) or halve it (in order to reach the next lowest).

Figure 1 is a graph showing partial tones set at constant distances along the horizontal axis and frequencies set out on the vertical axis. When the values from the previous table are plotted and joined together, the result will be a straight line, which demonstrates the correspondence of the frequencies in relationship to the partial tones.

The next graph (Figure 2 on page 23), demonstrates the frequencies in relationship to the keyboard of a piano. On a standard piano, the distance from one octave to another consists of about 6 $1/2$ in. or 16.5 cm. The thirteenth key on a piano is always the octave tone. If a graph were drawn of this, the result would a be a curve rather than a straight line. The curve in Figure 2 is known as an exponential curve because the frequencies increase in proportion to the keyboard in an exponential manner. To put it the other way around, the keyboard of a piano could be said to represent a logarithmic correspondence of frequencies. A slide rule demonstrates this clearly. The keyboard of a piano has the same relationship to the frequencies as the slide rule to the effective numbers. On a slide rule, the distance between one and two is as large as that between two and four, and four and eight. This means that the value of the numbers is doubled although the distance remains the same. This also applies to the keyboard of a piano. If you srike the 13th key to the right of the fundamental tone (as mentioned above), you will hear four times the frequency of the fundamental tone. This phenomenon can also be demonstrated on a guitar or any other stringed instrument. The frets are on the neck, and the second octave fret divides the string in a ratio of 1:4. The higher octaves can only be played as flageolet tones. The third octave divides the strings in a ratio of 1:8 and the fourth octave in a ratio of 1:16. The distances of the string are halved from octave to octave, while the resulting frequencies are doubled.

Figure 3 on page 24 demonstrates that the neck of a guitar is a logarithmic representation of the chromatic scale (represented in linear form on the keyboard of a piano) and a double logarithmic representation of the corresponding frequencies. If the keyboard is taken as a basic system of measurement, the neck of a guitar demonstrates a function to the keyboard, while the frequencies demonstrate an exponential function.

Seen from the point of view of mathematical correspondences, hearing can be compared to the keyboard of a piano. This fact is of great significance, for it can help us picture the relative size and interrelationship of all the values of natural phenomena (microcosm and macrocosm).

From now on, I will be using the octave as a unit of measurement that can be applied to astronomic periods, to the frequency sequences of the earth's atmosphere (spherics) and to vibrational microbiological phenomena. In this way I will prove that the octave is not only valid for audible frequencies but is applicable on a truly universal level. Whatever the field, the uniting factor is always the octave.

Apart from the prime or fundamental tone, the octave is the interval with the lowest degree of energetic resistance. All other tones vibrate with it and thus it plays a significant role in relationship to all other intervals, a fact which is not only applicable to music, but to other fields as well. In Figures 5 and 6, on pages 26 and 27 respectively, where the vibrations of the frequencies previously discussed are represented as curves, one can clearly see how many points of intersection the individual partial tones have in common with those of the fundamental tone. Figure 5 is of the vibration of the first four octave tones. The more mutual intersections occur in such a system, the less energy is needed to keep such a system going.

The rotation of the earth serves as an example of this. Measured against the fixed stars, the earth takes 23 hours and 56 minutes to rotate once around its own axis. Measured against the sun, around which the earth makes its yearly journey, the rotation takes exactly 24 hours. The difference is due to the earth's own movement, for a year has 365 $^1/_4$ mean sun days and 366 $^1/_4$ sidereal days. In other words, the difference of four minutes between a solar day and a sidereal day amounts to a whole day over the period of a year (see Figure 4 on page 25). Precise astronomic data with regard to this phenomenon is to be found in the Appendix, calculated to fractions of a second. Here I will restrict myself to round figures.

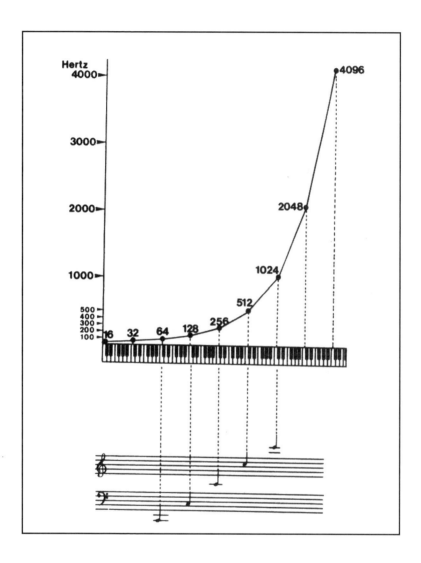

Figure 2. **Overtones and the piano keyboard**

The graph demonstrates the relationship of the octave overtones to their corresponding frequencies. The horizontal axis contains eight complete octaves, corresponding to the keyboard of a piano. The distance from one octave to another is constant in each case. The vertical axis shows the corresponding frequencies. The relationship is an exponential function.

12th fret « » octave

Figure 3. **Guitar**

In order to help the musician find the correct chords, the neck of a guitar is divided into frets. The distance from one fret to another becomes smaller and smaller the closer they get to the body, demonstrating a logarithmic relationship.

Figure 4. **A sidereal day and a mean sidereal day**

The earth rotates around its own axis in 23 hours and 56 minutes. Viewed from a certain location on the earth, the fixed stars will be in exactly the same position again once this period of time has lapsed. In other words, after this period of time, the same stars will pass through the meridian again. The earth circles the sun once a year, turning 336 ¼ times around its own axis. However, since the year only has 365 days, the so-called mean solar day is about four minutes longer than an earth day. The fact of the matter is that the earth turns by 361 degrees before the sun goes through the southern point, or the so-called meridian again. Seen from the earth, the position of the sun in relation to the fixed stars shifts every day by about one degree, which amounts to about 30 degrees in one month. This corresponds to the size of a sign in the zodiac.

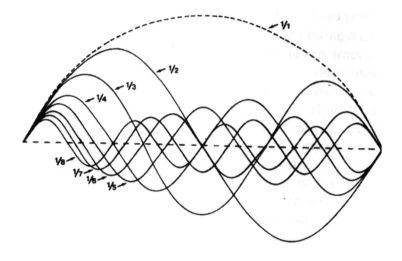

Figure 5. The first eight partial tones, represented as sine curves
     The sine curves of the first partial tones intersect the main axis 22 times.
The 23rd point of intersection corresponds to the first again.

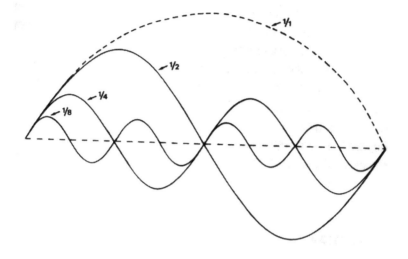

Figure 6. **Sine curves of the first four octave tones**
The sine curves of the first eight octave tones intersect the main axis eight times. The ninth point of intersection corresponds to the first again.

Like the vibration of an organ pipe or an oscillator, the rotation of the earth is a periodic occurrence, with the length of a period being a day. The frequency corresponds to half, or once every twelve hours. In this way, it is possible to construct a scale with all the frequencies of the upper octaves of an earth day and find out which natural phenomena befit them. We now turn to the earth day and its component part in detail. Anyone unsure about the meaning of fifths and major thirds, or who is afraid of numbers, can skip this part and go on to the section titled "Spherics and Proteins."

In many schools, a lesson lasts 45 minutes, and 45 minutes amounts to a 32nd part of a day. Since 32 belongs to the second power series (2, 4, 8, 16, 32, 64, 128, 265, etc.), being its fifth part, the length of 45 minutes corresponds to the period of the fifth upper octave of the day. While a school lesson cannot be regarded as a natural phenomenon, it is a unit of time that few of us have been able to evade. The relationship of a day to a school lesson can be visualized with the help of a piano. The deepest G on the piano has a frequency of about 24 hertz (which corresponds to the 21st octave of the day). The note found five octaves higher is the twice-accented g (g''), which is 32 times the frequency of the piano's deepest G. If both notes are struck at the same time, you will hear the time and frequency relationship of a day and a school lesson. One of the great adavantages of the octave as a system of measurement is that even very long periods can be transposed into audible form to demonstrate certain relationships. For example, should you want to hear the relationship of a day to a minute on an instrument, you could make use of this method, only you would have to include two fifths and a major third into your calculation as well as octaves. This is because the number 45 cannot be divided by 2, but only by 3 and 5. The tone of a quarter of an hour has a frequency three times higher than that of a school lesson. This means that it is two-twelfths higher than a g'' and is thus a d''''. This is a tone that can be played on the piano, but the tone of five minutes is $1/_{12}$ higher than that of 15 minutes. Starting out with a d'''', the result will be an a'''''. The tone of a minute lies two octaves and a major third over this a''''' and will be a very high c, a c′′′′′′′′ (a C accented eight times). However, this note lies beyond the range of human hearing.

In spite of this, the relationship of a day to a minute can be expressed in audible form, for we do not only hear tones, we can also hear rhythm and beat. The speed of a beat is determined by the given tempo, for example in beats per minte. Thus, all we need do is transpose the respective frequencies fives octaves down. The c′′′′′′′′ will become a C′′′ accordingly, and the low G will be transposed into a tempo of 45 beats per minute. With the help of a programmable synthesizer such as the Synclavier, it is very easy to play such a tone and beat togther. In order to hear the relationship of the day to hour, the point of departure should be the low G again, which has 24 hertz.

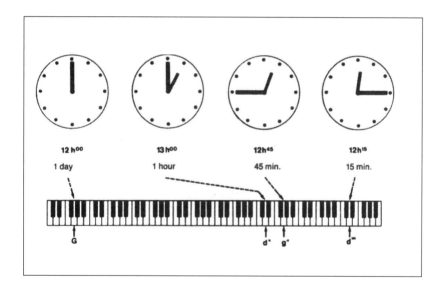

Figure 7. **The division of the day demonstrated on a keyboard**
Since the length of a day corresponds to the tone G, the tones of an hour, a school lesson (45 minutes), and a quarter of an hour can be calculated accordingly. In this way it is possible to demonstrate the length of the respective periods in relation to each other in audible form.

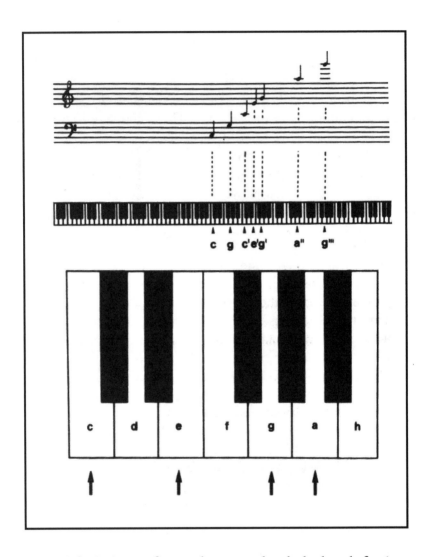

Figure 8. **Spherics in note form and transposed to the keyboard of a piano**

For the main part, the fundamental oscillations of the electromagnetic impulses from the earth's atmosphere are exact octave tones of the earth's rotation. Apart from the octave (G), the whole tone (A), and fourth (C) and major sixth (E) can also be observed.

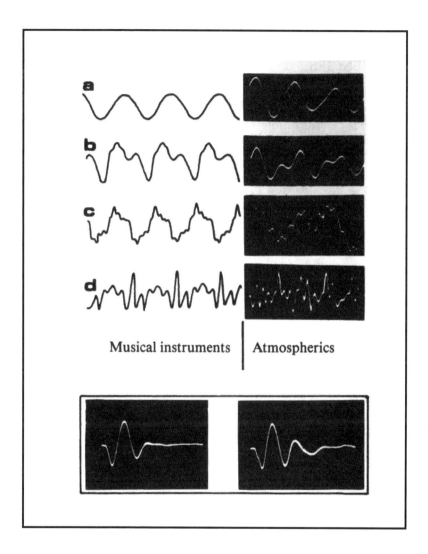

Figure 9. **Spherics.**

Upper diagram: Comparison of the oscillation of musical instruments and original atmospheric impulses: a) tuning fork, b) flute, c) clarinet, d) oboe.

Lower diagram: Two active 10-kilohertz impulses. Both illustrations have been taken from the "Technischer Informationsdienst."[8]

The day has 24 hours. If this number is factored into prime elements the following single factors will be obtained: 2 x 2 x 3 x 5. This indicates that we must take the frequency three octaves higher, and then another three, or, in other words, $^1/_{12}$. This first takes us three octaves higher than the low G, to the middle G, and the $^1/_{12}$ above results in a d" (twice-accented d). If both these tones are played simultaneously on the piano, you will hear the relationship of the day to the hour exactly 21 octaves higher than the original one. The day corresponds to G, the hour to D and the minute to C.

Now we have to calculate the tone of the seconds. A minute has 60 seconds. If 60 is factored into prime elements, the following factors will be obtained: 2 x 2 x 3 x 5. The frequency is thus taken two whole octaves above C, then a twelfth (an octave and a fifth) and then a major third in the second upper octave. Altogether, we now have five octaves, a fifth and a major third. The fifth from C leads to G sharp and the major third leads to C. Therefore, the tone of a second is a C. If you want to make music based on the tones of the day, the hour, minutes and seconds, the scale should involved the notes C, C sharp, D, and G.

Spherics and Proteins

Scientific discoveries often happen in quite different ways than what is popularly believed to be the case. For example, one discovery was made because a large Munich printing company wanted to know why the quality of their rotogravure printing changed with the weather. In rotogravure printing, the picture to be printed is transferred by photomechanical means onto a cylinder smeared with a thin glaze of protein made of thin layers of gelatine and then etched. Since results were not always satisfactory at the printing company of F. Bruckman of Munich, the engineer Hans Baumer was hired to find out why. The only known fact was that a certain role was played by the weather, especially with regard to the humidity outside. Baumer made a list of the dates when unsatisfactory results occured and compared them with meteorological data, but he could not discover any kind of relationship. He then had the ingenious idea of examining the weather one or two days after the printing, and discovered that the gelatin did indeed react to weather conditions that would occur one or two days later. Could the gelatin foretell future weather conditions?

Baumer's task was now to determine the natural phenomena that preceded certain weather constellations, and the way in which they affected protein gelatin. After many years of investigation, his search finally led him to the so-called spherics, also known as the atmospherics. Spherics are short electromagnetic impulses which are continuously formed in the atmosphere of the earth. These impulses, which occur in different frequency bands, have a determining effect on the weather. Hans Baumer commented on his findings in the following way:

> With the help of a radio receiver it was possible to continuously record a narrow band of atmospherics in the ranges of 10 and 27 kilohertz. The receiver was electronically adjusted to only register atmospherics within a circumference of 400 to 500 kilometers of the observation post. Registration took place at Pfaffenhofen/Ilm, which is about 30 km north of Munich, from May 1978 until the end of April 1979, excluding nine days lost due to technical failure.[9]

With the help of magnetic wide-band antennae, it was possible to determine spectral concentrations of frequency in over 35,000 individual impulse analysis tests. The spectral maxima were found in narrow bands in the following areas:

4150.83 hertz	12452.52 hertz
6226.26 hertz	28018.17 hertz
8301.26 hertz	49810.08 hertz
10377.10 hertz	

Baumer said,

Apart from the fact that the additional frequencies occur without exception in surprisingly narrow-banded ranges, the most striking factor is the 'harmonical' means of distribution. They are quite clearly in simple numerical relationship to each other, corresponding to the octave, the fifth, the fourth, and the third, etc. in the field of sound. It is possible that this phenomenon will lead us to a clue in the investigation of the conditions under which atmospherics occur and travel, for it seems that atmoshperics can be regarded as a transmission system with nonlinear characteristics. If a simple oscillation encounters a nonlinear transmission system, the result will be that a whole series of harmonic oscillations will come out at the other end along with the simple oscillation. In this case, the general principle of oscillation has been derived from the field of acoustics, but if applied in similar fashion to the 'atmosophere,' the spectrum of atmospherics described can be concluded to proceed from a simple oscillation.[9] (same as previous note)

The simple oscillation responsible for the occurrence of atmospherics is nothing other than the rotation of the earth. Hans Baumer made atmospheric frequencies audible in exactly the same way that I did with astronomic periods, by applying the law of the octave. In the process, a surprising factor came to light—the tones produced were identical. Whether a diatonic, naturally-tuned scale is based on the roation of the earth, or on spherics, is basically one and the same thing. Indeed, there will only be a slight difference of a 1,000th of a part, so slight that it cannot be heard.

In the following table, the first column shows the series of atmospheric frequencies that were registered, while the second contains the corresponding audible freqeuncies, exaclty five octaves deeper. In the third column, the exact octave tones of the earth are printed in bold face while the fourth lists the corresponding notes. In not a single case does the difference between the octave tones of the weather and the earth's rotation consist of more than .73 parts per thousand.

This can surely be no coincidence. Indeed, it is apparent that a causal relationship exists between the rotation of the earth and spherics frequencies. The physical law common to both is that of the octave.

Furthermore, the registered weather frequencies display an extremely high degree of harmonious interrelationship. Apart from one case, these relationships are analogous to simple musical proportions, the exception being the atmospheric frequency of 28,018.17 hertz, which corresponds to the tone a′′. From c on, is the only tone that will combine with c, and moreover, it does not occur in the natural overtone series. This frequency also plays a special role in meteorology, being the only atmospheric frequency allocated to vertical air-mass movements known as turbulences. Whether seen from the point of view of music or atmospherics, a is a combined tone.

ORIGINAL SPHERICS FREQUENCIES	SPHERICS FREQUENCIES :2^5	DIATONIC TONES FROM THE SCALE OF AN EARTH DAY	NOTE
4,150.84	129.714	**129.808**	c
6,226.26	194.571	**194.571**	g
8,301.26	259.414	**259.617**	c′
10,377.10	324.284	**324.521**	e′
12,452.52	389.141	**389.425**	g′
28,018.17	875.568	**876.206**	a′′
49,810.08	1556.699	**1,557.699**	g′′

Proteins Again

The investigation of printing gelatin demonstrates that electro-magnetic atmospheric impulses can modify the structure of protein molecules. However, protein molecules are found not only in printing gelatin, but also in the human body, where they participate in certain biological processes.

The blueprint for the different kinds of proteins is woven into the DNA chains. DNA is short for deoxyribonucleic acid and the DNA chains are genes, or bearers of genetic information. The blueprint and function plan of the organism are contained in nucleic acids. Apart from the DNA, which passes on genetic information to the next generation by means of self-duplication (identical replicas), there are also RNAs, or ribonucleic acids, which make use of genetic information in order to control the formation of different proteins. Quite independently of each other, two scientists observed that both the DNA and the RNA chains have a very special resonance maximum. This maximum corresponds exactly to an octave tone of the earth's rotation! Reasearch carried out by Fritz Popp (formerly of Marburg University and now at Kaiserlautern University, both in West Germany) and studies by Wilfried Krüger confirm the observation of Hans Baumer that protein compounds react to certain frequencies. In this respect, the octave frequency of the earth's rotation plays a role of special significance. Wilfried Krüger correlates atoms and molecules to tones by applying analogies between the spin of an atom and harmonical laws.

As he wrote in his book, *Das Universum Singt* :

> My scale model of the four different accented A''' at the top... and G is the basic electron of the DNA-RNA ribbons. A and G represent not only the basis and beginning of our tone system, but also the basis, axis and cover of the framework and belt of the nucleic acid ribbons. These in turn act as the bridge between the world of indivisible quanta and that of composite matter . . .[10]

Fritz Popp followed a completely different approach in studying the maximum resonance of the DNA, which are associated with the transmission of human and animal genes. For many years, his area of research has been the so-called photon emission of living cells. Every living being radiates. In esoteric circles this radiation is called the aura, while scientists and doctors call it photon emission. Photons are the matter particles and information carriers of light, for light consists of both waves and matter. The light radiation of a cell or living being, which can be registered with the help of complicated apparatus, differs according to the condition of the cell involved and thus changes in photon emission, and makes it possible to ascertain the condition of the object under investigation. In this way, Fritz Popp determined that the highest resonance maximum of the DNA was at a wavelength of 351 millimicrons (.000,000,351 meter). This corresponds to the frequency of 854 trillion hertz (854,000,000,000,000), which corresponds to the 66th octave of the earth's rotation. The harmonic structure of the resonance of an atom's spin and Fritz Popp's resonance maximum both confirm that DNA and RNA chains are in a state of harmonious resonance to the octave tones of the earth's rotation. When one considers that life on earth developed under the given astronomical condition, and that the shortest astronomical period to influence this development was that of the earth's rotation, none of these will seem at all surprising. In the development of life, weather frequencies, or atmospherics, acted as a kind of intermediate amplifier of this basic vibration. Once again, the binding link of all these vibrational systems is the octave.

The Tones of Our Solar System

In the same way that it is possible to determine the tone of an earth day, the astronomic periods and the whole of our solar system can also be made audible–with the help of the octave. The earth has three basic tones, that of the day, the year, and of the Platonic year. The Platonic year is the rotation of the earth's axis. The earth's axis does not stand still, but describes a rotation which takes 25,290 years. This accounts for the change in the date of the vernal equinox, which is the position of the sun at the beginning of spring. Measured against the fixed stars, this position is one that is always in movement, and the location at any given time is an indication of the aeon involved. At the moment, the vernal equinox is moving from the age of Pisces into the age of Aquarius, which explains why there is so much talk about the age of Aquarius and a New Age.

As already mentioned, there are two kinds of days, one being the so-called mean solar day (which lasts exactly 24 hours), and the other being the sidereal day, which lasts 23 hours and 56 minutes.

At this point, I would like once again to demonstrate the method of transposing astronomic periods into musical tones, using the earth day as an example. The earth day has 24 hours and 86,400 seconds (24 x 60 x 60 = 86,400). The reciprocal value is formed out of this number (using the "l/x" key on a pocket calculator). The reciprocal obtained must now be multiplied by 2 until the medium range of audible frequencies has been reached. If the frequency of the earth day is multiplied by two 24 times, the result will be 194.18 hertz, while multiplication of two 25 times results in a frequency of 388.36 hertz.

Figure 10. The Earth's Rotation and the Octave

Mean solar day	24 hours	194.18 Hz
Sidereal day	23 hours 56 min.	194.71 Hz
Year	356.242 days	136.10 Hz
Platonic year	25,290 years	172.06 Hz

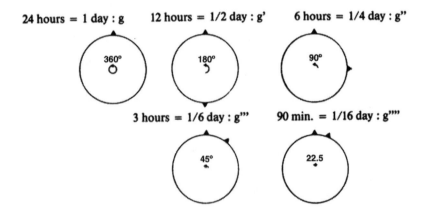

The Tones of the Earth

An earth day, which corresponds to a full rotation of the earth on its own axis, produces the fundamental tone (g). Half a rotation results in the first octave (g'), a quarter rotation results in the second octave (g") and an eighth of a rotation results in the third (g"'). A sixteenth of a rotation results in the fourth octave (g"").

The Tones of the Moon

There are a number of lunar rhythms, such as:
— the *culmination period* of the moon: the length of time from one culmination (or meridian transition) to another;
— the *synodic month*: the mean time from one new moon to another or from one full moon to another;
— the *sidereal month:* the mean time of the moon's revolution in its orbit around the earth, measured against the fixed stars;
— the *rotation of the moon:* the rotation of the moon around its own axis. This is bound by the period of the orbit due to gravitational interaction with the earth. The frequency is identical to that of the sidereal month;
— the *metonic cycle:* a period of 19 years (or 235 synodic months) after which the phases of the moon return to a particular date in the calendar year. For example, if somebody was born at full moon, it will be full moon again on his 19th or 38th birthday;
— the *nodical month:* the mean time of the moon's revolution in its orbit from ascending node to ascending node (the points at which the orbit of the moon intersects the ecliptic). The nodical month is also known as the draconic period;
— the *apsis orbit:* the point in the moon's elliptical orbit where its distance from the earth is either greatest (the apogee) or least (the perigee);
— the *saros cycle:* a lunar cycle of eclipses, consisting of 223 synodic orbits or 18 years and approximately 11 days, at the end of which the centers of sun and moon return so closely to their relative positions at the beginning that all eclipses of the period recur approximately as before.

Culmination period	24 hours 25 min.	187.61 Hz
Synodic month	29.5306 days	210.42 Hz
Sidereal month	27.3217 days	227.43 Hz
Metonic cycle	6939.6882 days	229.22 Hz
Apsis orbit	3232.6854 days	246.04 Hz
Nodical month	6793.3951 days	234.16 Hz
Saros cycle	6585.3211 days	231.16 Hz

The Tone of the Sun

The tone of the sun is more complicated to calculate. Please see Chapter 7.

Sun tone   0.000030948 seconds   126.22 Hz

The Tones of the Planets

The tones of the planets are calculated in the same way as those for the earth and the moon. The following table presents the tones of the sidereal orbits of the planets. Since the rotation cycle of some planets has not yet been determined, the planets in question are not included. Moreover, the position of the planets in the ecliptic has far more effect on the earth than their rotation. The planetoid Chiron, which was identified by Charles T. Koval on November 1, 1977, and which has since become very fashionable in astrological circles, is not included because the mean period of the revolution of this planetoid, which steers a very eccentric course though the heavens, has not yet been determined. Furthermore, due to the instability of the orbit, the period of revolution is not very constant and varies between 49 and 51 years. Were one to proceed from a mean value, such as that of 50 years, the result would be an F in the 38th octave, with about 175 hertz. This corresponds approximately to the tone of the double star Sirius and to the tone of the Platonic year, which consists of 172.06 hertz.

Mercury, the planet closest to the sun, has the shortest period of revolution, while Pluto, which is furthest away, has the longest. Since Mercury and Venus lie between the earth and the sun, their orbits last less than an earth year, while the orbits of the planets positioned beyond the earth are correspondingly longer.

Mercury	0.24082 years	141.27 Hz
Venus	0.61521 years	221.23 Hz
Earth	1.000 year	136.10 Hz
Mars	1.8808089 years	144.72 Hz
Jupiter	11.86223 years	183.58 Hz
Saturn	29.45774 years	147.85 Hz
Uranus	84.01529 years	207.36 Hz
Neptune	167.78830 years	211.44 Hz
Pluto	248.4301 years	140.25 Hz

CHAPTER 3
THE FREQUENCY OF AN EARTH DAY

The principle of dynamic activity corresponding to the physical level.

The tone of an earth day is 'G,' whereby it must be pointed out that there are two very similar earth day tones, namely that of a mean solar day and that of a sidereal day. In the 24th octave, these tones have the following frequencies:

Mean solar day	194.18 hertz
Sidereal day	194.71 hertz

In the 25th octave, which is the position of the "g" on the violin clef, both these tones have double the frequency:

Mean solar day	388.36 hertz
Sidereal day	389.42 hertz

The color of an earth day ranges from orange-red to red and corresponds to the 65th octave of an earth day. From a psychological point of view, these colors have to do with will power, impulsiveness and a dynamic attitude in general.

The color orange-red has a direct influence on the process of cell division. In Canada, for example, Professor Max Lüscher proved in several series of experiments that the growth of testes in drakes can be controlled by the use of color. Two groups of drakes were kept under different colored lights in otherwise identical conditions. The testes of drakes reared beneath an orange-red light grew twice as fast as those of drakes kept below pale blue light.[11]

From the standpoint of harmonics, the results of this experiment seem very logical. The color orange-red is the 65th octave of an earth day and the maximum resonance of the DNA chains (carriers of genetic information) lies exactly in the middle of the 66th octave of the day (as mentioned in Chapter 2). This maximum is the first overtone of the color orange-red. Since the tone that vibrates most strongly with the fundamental tones is the first overtone, this color also entails the vibration of the DNA chains, thus multiplying their vibration rate. This explains why this color has such a vitalizing effect. If you wear orange-red clothing for awhile you will certainly notice this. The invigorating effect of orange-red is also undoubtedly due to the dynamic effect of this color on cell division. This was intuitively understood in ancient India, where the monks, known as sannyasins, always wore orange-red robes and still continue to do so. Music composed in "G" is also very stimulating and is therefore not recommended for Roman Catholic priests.

In my opinion, the Roman Catholic Church seems to propagate a very non-biological form of religion. It portrays the progenitive act, which is a truly creative process, as something sinful and dirty. The Immaculate Conception is nothing more than the suppression of sexuality on a godly level. The God of the Christians and Jews is more like a senior prosecutor than a God full of the joy of life. His only means of communication is via the Word and He is constantly telling us what to do and what not to do. The effect of all this is visible in the importance attached to laws and prohibitions in societies influenced by Christianity. The Indian gods were very different; they spent their time dancing and singing. Krishna is always portrayed holding a flute, and Shiva, the creator and destroyer of all life, invented the vina, one of the oldest ritual instruments in India. Shiva is the cosmic dancer–Shiva Mahadeva, the master of breath, sound and movement.

In Greek mythology, Aphrodite, the goddess assigned to the planet Venus, is the embodiment of a principle diametrically opposed to that of the Immaculate Conception. Aphrodite is the goddess of opulent fertility, love, charm and grace. She was married to Hephaestus, but that did not prevent her from having love affairs with Aries, the God

Figure 11. **Dancing Shiva**

of War, and Adonis, a beautiful young boy. The name Adonis almost certainly derives from a Semitic language and is identical to *Adonai,* which means "my lord." If European judges who grew up under Christian influence had passed judgment on the Greek gods, most of them would have landed in prison for sodomy and fornication. It is typical of the West to admire Greek cultural artifacts and temples, deeming them worthy of preservation, yet to abhor both the orgies that took place in these temples and the mentality and ideology that made them possible. It is inconsistent to admire the cultural assets of a nation while condemning the culture that produced them.

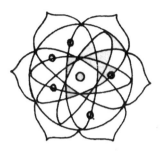

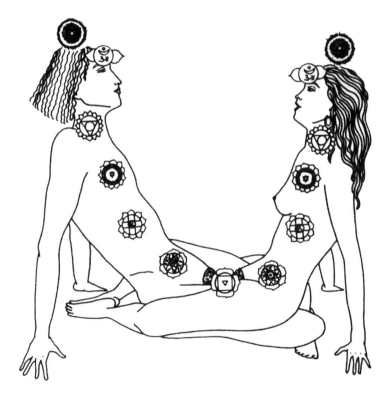

Figure 12. **A Tantric scene**

Of all religious teachings, Tantrism is probably the one most closely adapted to the biological functioning of the human body. Its highest religious ritual is the union of man and woman in the sexual act. All Tantric rituals aim to perfect the progenitive act and achieve absolute ecstasy. It is surely of significance that the members of one race are conceived in exaltation and rapture, while for centuries, others were conceived in the consciousness of sex being something dirty, as is still the case in the West. Tantra is the erotic path to ecstasy!

Use of the Earth Day Tone in Everyday Life

Tuning forks can be used to either stimulate or relax the whole or part of the body. They can also be applied to acupuncture points with similar effect.

Fig. 13. The vibrational behavior of tuning forks
When a tuning fork is struck, the prongs vibrate in a sideways direction and the shaft in a vertical one. This is because the vibration is diverted at the meeting point of the prongs.

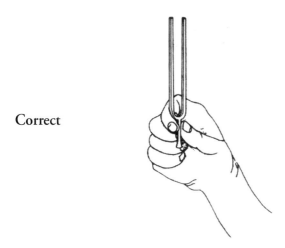

Correct

Figure 14. **How to hold a tuning fork**
A tuning fork will not vibrate if you hold the prongs or even touch them. Make sure to hold the shaft between your forefinger and thumb, as illustrated above.

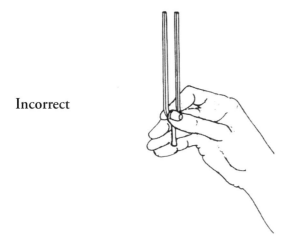

Incorrect

Figure 15. **How not to hold a tuning fork**
Here the tuning fork is being held at the bottom of the prongs and will not vibrate correctly.

The tone "G" generally has a stimulating and tonic effect, while "C sharp" (the tone of an earth year–see Chapter 4) will tend to calm you down. For this reason, it is advisable to use the "G" day tone in the morning or before starting any kind of activity. It is better to use the "C sharp" tone when you want to relax or go to sleep. The "G" tone has an energizing and activating effect and you will feel it most strongly when you hold the tuning fork between your legs. You can do this standing up or lying down. If you are a man, you should hold the tuning fork between the anus and the scrotum. If you are a woman, it should be held between the anus and the vulva. The vibration of the tuning fork will stimulate the sexual organs and intensify arousal, for it kindles the fire of kundalini, the snake power that lies sleeping in the lowest chakra. In his book, *Die Welt des Yoga*, Hans David describes the lowest chakra in the following way:

> The muladhara chakra stands for sexual feelings. The power of this chakra and the free flow of its energy release a vital charge of energy that affects one's dealings with life in general. It takes on its most refined form in the act of love. Sexual energy is dynamic, it is the energy of life itself. All bodily functions are dependent on the free flow of muladhara energy. In contrast, people with neurotic disturbances display an inability to release energy. A blockage of energy in this chakra is associated with a general "freezing" of psychosomatic functions.[12]

The use of a G tuning fork in the area of the second, or "svadhistana" chakra, which stands for excretion and for human relations, will have an astonishingly invigorating effect.

> Disturbances in this chakra are manifested in the form of cramps in the entire pelvic region and in the legs, while, on an emotional level, the free flow of energy is blocked. Feelings are held back and suppressed and become hardened as a result. The person thus affected finds it difficult to express these suppressed feelings. The state of tension can be seen in the way the bottom is pulled together, resulting in a fold beneath the buttocks. Strict toilet training in childhood results in too much attention being placed on this point in later life, resulting in a need for cleanliness, order and obedience.[13]

The same author comments on the second chakra in the following way: Stimulation of the following points is recommended for men who feel a burning sensation in the penis when they urinate. The first point is 50 on the bladder meridian, which is a handbreadth away from the midpoint between the legs on the lower edge of the buttocks (see Figure 18 on page 53). The effect can be increased and supported by massaging the heels. Further points are 11 and 12, which are on the kidney meridian, the only organ meridian not intersected by any other meridian. These points, which are very effective, are found about a handbreadth away from the sides of the navel in the lower third of the stomach (see Figure 19 on page 54). Another effective point is 10, which is to be found in the hollow of the knee on the bladder meridian. Further points of interest are 19 and 20 on the large intestine meridian, below the nose (see Figure 22 on page 55). It may seem strange to some readers that a point below the nose is able to affect the kidneys, the bladder, the penis, the large intestine and the anus. Remember, however, that energy flows throughout the whole of the body. If you get wet feet in cold, rainy weather, you'll probably get a cold as a result. How do the feet affect the nose?

The answer is that several meridians end in the feet. If these are affected by the cold, other parts of the body will react. The organism's immunity to disease is impaired as a result, and it will no longer be able to combat virus infections successfully. Colds, for example, are caused by viruses, which is why there is no cure for a cold. Of course, the symptoms can be alleviated with drops, tablets and creams, and you can take something to help you breathe freely through your nose, but you can only cure the cause by destroying the viruses involved. The only thing that can do that is your immune system. Therefore, when you have a cold, the most important thing to do is to stimulate and improve your natural immunity.

You can only have ecstatic sex when your excretory organs are functioning well. In other words, if there's a feeling of pressure on the bladder, you won't be able to let go when you make love. For this reason, it is not only important to concentrate on your sexual energies to get more out of sex, but you must also make sure that your bowels and bladder are in good shape.

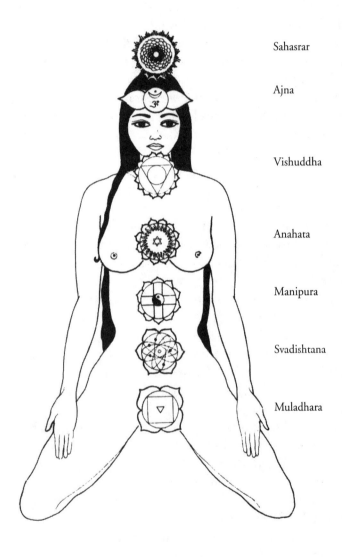

Sahasrar

Ajna

Vishuddha

Anahata

Manipura

Svadishtana

Muladhara

Figure 16. **The Seven Main Chakras**

Chakra	Traditional symbols	Location	Psychological level (acc. to modern psychological findings)
Muladhara		Perineum	The unconscious, unawakened person, confined in himself. Static energy. Inability to affirm life.
Svadisthana		3rd coccygeal	Awakening of sexual energy; vertebrae the person begins to open himself up. Slow-moving vibrations and emotions such as desire, longing, jealousy, anger, etc.
Manipura (Hara)		Navel and 3rd lumbar vertebrae	Desire for power, conquest and possession. Intense activity, ambition.
Anahata		5th dorsal vertebrae	In this chakra opposites are united by love. Death of the personal and egoistic "I." The person opens himself up. Empathy.
Vishuddha		Cervical vertebrae, throat pit	The level of expression; the urge to purify oneself and look within in order to feel the presence of God. Desire to purify one's energies.
Ajna		Between the eyebrows	High spiritual experiences. Bliss. Unity of within and without.
Sahasrara		Central point at the top of the head	Cosmic unity with God. Divine inspiration, supramental intuition.

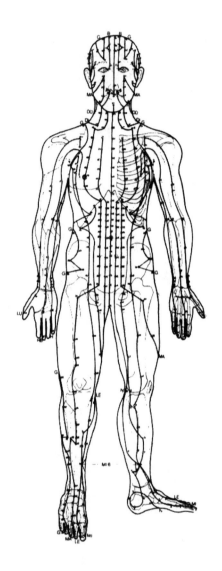

Figure 17. **Table of meridians**
In acupuncture, cetain point of the meridians are activated with a needle in
order to treat corresponding organs.

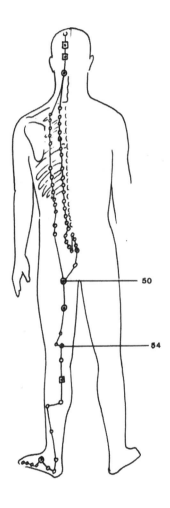

Figure 18. **Points 50 and 54 on the bladder meridian**

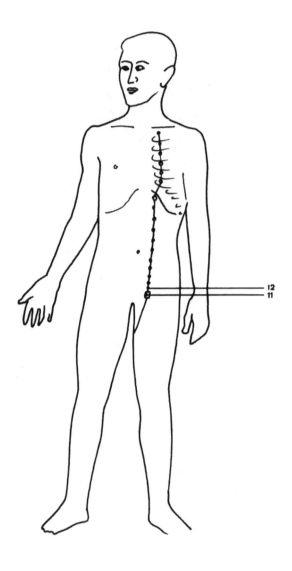

Figure 19. **Points 11 and 12 on the kidney meridian**

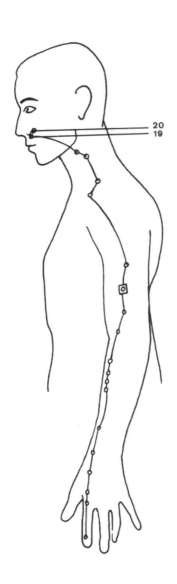

20
19

Figure 20. **Points 19 and 20 on the large intestine meridian**

CHAPTER 4
THE FREQUENCY OF AN EARTH YEAR

The Principle of Relaxation Corresponding to the Spiritual Level

The tone of an earth year is "om." Om is the primordial vibration or the ever-sounding tone, as it has always been called in India. In our tonal system, the frequency of this vibration corresponds to a "C sharp." In the 32nd octave of an earth year, this tone oscillates at a frequency of 136.10 hertz, and in the 33rd octave at a frequency of 272.20 hertz. The frequency of an earth year tone consists of 136.1 hertz, a result arrived at in the following way.

First the year is broken down into seconds. A day has 86,400 seconds and a year has 365.242 days. Multiply the days by the seconds and the answer will be 31,556,925.9747 seconds. The reciprocal value of this number can now be calculated, using the 1/x function on a pocket calculator and the result multiplied by two 32 times. The frequency will be 136 hertz. The corresponding color is a green turquoise with a touch of blue.

Music in Harmony with the Earth is the Secret of Indian Meditation Music

The audience waits in anticipation. In a concert hall lit by sparkling candelabras, musicians throng onto the stage and take their seats. They leaf through the score and take up their instruments. The pianist strikes a key. A clear tone rings out and the audience settles beneath its thick tapestry. As the pianist repeats a note, the room erupts into a flurry of musicians tuning violins and cellos, oboes and bassoons to this tone; the concert can begin.

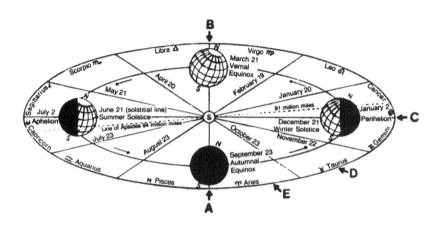

Figure 21. **The year and the octave**

At the beginning of spring, the sun is in 0 degrees Aries (A), where it will be again after another year. Once half a year has passed, the sun will be at 0 degrees Libra (B), which is the beginning of autumn. This point corresponds to the first octave of the year. After quarter of a year, the sun will be at 0 degrees Cancer (C), which is the beginning of summer. This point corresponds to the second octave of the year. After an eighth of year, the sun will be at 15 degrees Taurus (D), which corresponds to the third octave of the year. The position of the sun after a sixteenth of a year, at 22 ¹/₂ degrees Aries, corresponds to the fourth octave of the year.

Silence. The conductor comes out onto the stage, bows to the enthusiastic applause of the audience with a broad smile and turns to the musicians. With his back to the audience, he gives the orchestra a searching glance. Then he nods his head, lifts his hands and gives the signal to play the first bar.

Every lover of classical music who prefers listening to a live orchestra to a canned version is familiar with this ritual in which the instruments of the orchestra are tuned to one common pitch.

In India, a lot more time is spent on tuning-up, especially before sitar performances, where it takes on the character of meditation. The sitar is the most widely-played stringed instrument on the Indian subcontinent and has a cultural status comparable to that of the violin in the West. A sitar is generally equipped with seven playing strings, which are plucked with a kind of thimble made of iron or silver wire, and a dozen or more sympathetic strings which resound to the notes played.

Since the sound of a sitar is mainly determined by the resonance of the overtones of the plucked strings, the sympathetic strings have to be tuned very exactly. This is the reason why tuning-up takes longer in India than in the West. Moreover, during this prelude, known as "alapa," the musician not only tunes his instrument to the keynote, called the "sadja" or the "father of the others," he also attunes himself to it, and gives the audience the opportunity to do so, too. According to Indian tradition, the "sadja" (or "sa" for short), is the everlasting, never-ceasing tone. It stands for the primordial vibration, which is called "nada" and which is expressed as "Om." "Om" in turn corresponds to the "Amen" of Christianity. "Amen" means nothing other than "so be it." "Om" is also an expression of the primordial vibration, which manifests in the everlasting, never-ceasing tone. The secret of the meditative effect of India's music lies in this primordial tone. The pitch to which sitars are tuned, and on which the holy "om" is sung, corresponds approximately to the "C sharp" in the small octave of the present-day tuning system. The frequency of the "sadja," which oscillates once in a 136th part of a second, can be doubled, thus determining its lower octave tones. If

Figure 22. **The Om symbol**
In India, Om is the symbol of the primordial vibration. It is sung in
"C sharp" and corresponds to the 32nd octave tone of the earth year.

this is done 32 times exactly, the resulting frequency will be as slow as the amount of time it takes the earth to circle the sun. In other words, it will last a whole year. The string giving the fundamental tone on a sitar is tuned to the sadja tone, oscillating at exactly the same frequency as the overtone of the 32nd octave of an earth year. For this reason, it is called the tone of an earth year. Thus, a sitar is tuned in exact harmony to the movement of the earth around the sun. Therefore, once a sitar has been tuned up during the "alapa," not only the instruments, but also the musicians and the audience will be attuned to this "everlasting tone," which reverberates within us whenever this kind of meditative music is played. This can easily be proved by comparing the tone of a 136 hertz tuning fork to original Indian sitar music. You can also try meditating to this tone, or simply humming or singing it.

Another, and perhaps the best way of proving this is to strike a tuning fork with a frequency of 136 hertz and press the shaft against the bottom of the breastbone. The whole chest will begin to reverberate and if you now begin to hum, you will do so at the right tone. The longer you sing "om" in this way, the more you will become one with this primordial cosmic vibration.

It is interesting to note that the Indians arrived at this tone, which we calculated with the help of mathematics, simply through intuition and meditation. This gives rise to the thought that the human mind and its faculties of perception are closely oriented to physical and harmonic laws. Indeed, true religion has little to do with dogma; what counts here is religious perception and experience:

"Om" — it is as it is. The more we are united to the great oneness, the greater will be the consciousness that nothing separates us from the universe and that we ourselves are part of the total cosmos. When the universe is reflected in each and every one of us in this way and we are able to really hear and attune ourselves to cosmic vibrations, we will no longer have a need for gurus, priests and Popes. Instead, we will begin to sense the way of all things and, in doing so, will become the way itself.[14]

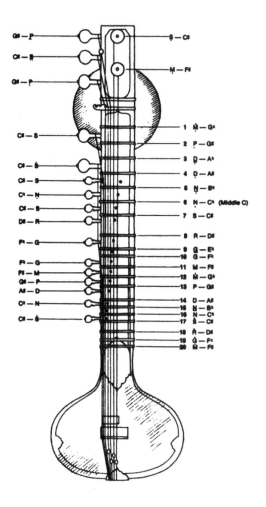

Figure 23. Tuning a sitar to the fundamental tone

The fundamental tone is a C sharp, keyed slightly lower than is usual in Europe and North America. In India, this fundamental tone is called sa or sadja and corresponds to the frequency of 136.10 hertz.

Morphogenetic Images and the Story of the Hundredth Monkey

For hundreds of years, the monkeys that lived on a South Seas island used to dig potatoes out of the earth and eat them up, dirty as they were. One day, one of the monkeys got the genial idea of washing his potatoes before eating them, and lo and behold, he no longer needed to crunch sand and stones along with his meal. Now other monkeys saw this and began to imitate him. They were imitated by other monkeys and these were imitated by more monkeys until, suddenly, something went click. The hundredth monkey had dipped his potato into water. The collective energy was consolidated into a "morphogenetic field" that linked the monkeys on a neighboring island, and they started washing their potatoes, too. No other form of communication took place. John Lilly calls this kind of knowledge transfer "ecco-connection," which basically means being in contact with the "Earth Coincidence Control Office." [15, 16, 17] The British biologist Rupert Shaldrake defines this phenomenon as the perception of so-called "morphogenetic fields" or "images." [18] He has postulated the theory that information known to a certain species, whether animal or human, is also available to other species belonging to the same family, even if they live in other parts of the world. For example, when many people think one thought, it will be picked up by many others. This is similar to the phenomenon Carl Gustav Jung called "synchronicity." [19]

Once you begin to attune yourself to the tone of an earth year, meditating to it and letting it reverberate within you, you will not only be one with the movement of the earth but also with all others whose meditation is attuned to this tone. Since this includes the saddhus of India and the monks of Tibet, whose bells also ring this tone, you will be in spiritual contact with these holy people. When you tune into this vibration you will participate in their peace of mind, becoming part of the "morphogenetic field" of all those already in harmony due to regular meditation. When you sing "om" to this tone, do not do so in the way you sing at school or church. Let it resound in your throat in such a way that the overtones become audible. This is known as overtone singing and is wide-spread in India. In recent times it has become fashionable in Europe and America, but it is not merely a fad. For a start, you can sing considerably longer in this way without getting tired and it also massages the head from within, which is very beneficial for the general sense of well-being. There are quite a few overtone singers who teach this technique at weekend seminars. It is certainly not difficult to learn. The best-known overtone singers in German-speaking countries are Michael Vetter,[20, 21] Roberto Lanieri and Stephanie Wolff.[22]

Use of C Sharp, the Earth Year Tone, in Everyday Life

This tone is suitable for every kind of meditation. Unlike the earth day tone, best used on waking up and before engaging in some kind of activity, this tone can be used at any time. It is very relaxing and soothing. Two meridians carry the vibration of the year tone to the rest of the body in a very intense and pleasant manner. These are the Ren-mai meridian, also referred to as the "Conception Vessel," and the Du-mai meridian, or "Governing Vessel." Due to the function of these meridians, they exert a strong effect on the mind and psyche.

The Ren-mai meridian runs up the middle of the body from the genital area to the mouth, via the navel, stomach, chest and throat. The most suitable points for transferring the vibrations of a tuning fork to this meridian are at points 16 and 17, both of which are situated at the lower end of the breastbone (see Figure 24 on page 64). If a vibrating tuning fork attuned to the tone of the earth year is held at either of these points, the whole chest will begin to reverberate as though a deep tone were being hummed. The use of a tuning fork at these points will lead to a pleasant and relaxed feeling of well-being.

The Du-mai meridian runs from the anus, where it surfaces, along the middle of the body via the spine, neck, and over the skull to the mouth (see Figure 25 on page 65). The points to treat on this meridian are numbers 1 and 2, which are very difficult to treat on oneself, however. The best way of treating these points is to either lie on your

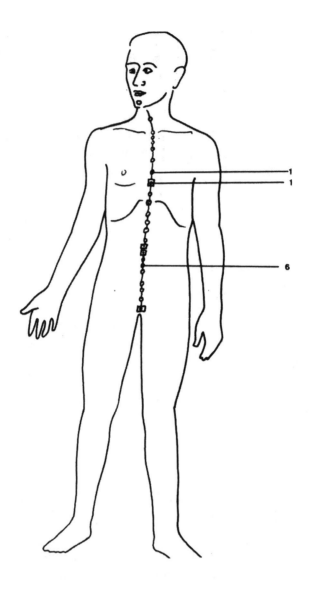

Figure 24. **Illustration of the Ren-mai meridian, showing the location of points 16 and 17**

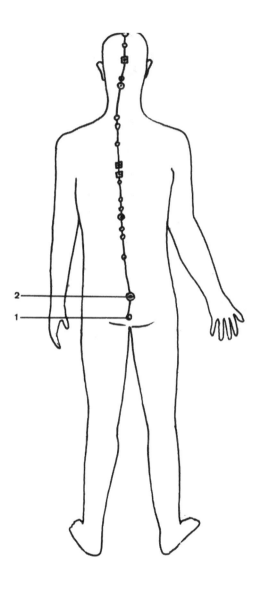

Figure 25. **Illustration of the Du-mai meridian, showing the location of points 1 and 2**

stomach or stand with your hands hanging loosely at your sides and have someone treat these points for you. Treatment of this meridian has a soothing and also pain-relieving effect on different areas of the body. Point 1 is found at the outermost point of the coccyx and point 2 is found at its upper end. Treating these points with the earth year tone will have a very relaxing effect on the buttocks.

Kundalini energy, which starts at the bottom of the spine, cannot rise up through the body when it is cramped in at the base of the spine. The fact that this is frequently the case is proved by the number of people who are constipated or who have hemorrhoids. A person who has relaxed buttocks will be able to let his energy flow much freer when he makes love than will someone who is tense in this area. It is with good reason that point 1 of the Du-mai meridian is known as the "increase in strength and joy of life" point.

If you want to treat this point with C sharp, hold the shaft of the tuning-fork against it until it ceases to vibrate. This will take about two minutes. Repeat, until you feel a pleasant feeling of relaxation, which should soon set in. You can also try out this tone on other points every now and then and you will soon begin to sense the course of the meridians through the body. When experienced in this way, there is no need to learn the meridians by referring to a textbook.*

•The application of tuning forks is primarily for the enhancement of relaxation, joy and happiness, which are the foundations for health and well-being. It is important to note that the therapeutic value of tuning fork treatment cannot replace medical treatment. All serious complaints should be treated by a doctor or by a licensed health practitioner.

CHAPTER 5
THE FREQUENCY OF THE PLATONIC YEAR

The Principle of Joyous Spirit

The duration of the Platonic year, which is about 25,920 years, represents the amount of time the axis of the earth takes to complete a full rotation. The vernal equinox journeys through each of the signs of the zodiac in this time. The vernal equinox is the point at which the equator (which is at right angles to the earth's axis) intersects the ecliptic (or zodiac). In other words, the vernal equinox is the position of the sun at the beginning of spring. During this time the sun is found between Pisces and Aquarius. The vernal equinox takes an average of 2,160 years to travel through a sign of the zodiac. This period of time is known as an "age." Presently, the age of Pisces is coming to an end and Aquarius is beginning. It is not possible to state exactly when one age ends and the other begins, because the signs overlap to a certain extent. Moreover, there is no absolute zero point in the zodiac. The change from one age to another takes place slowly, over a period of many years.

The tone of the Platonic year is an "F." In the 47th octave, the frequency of the Platonic year measures 172.06 hertz and in the 48th it measures 344.12 hertz. The corresponding color is violet. No areas of the solar spectrum have the same frequency as that of the Platonic year: at the red end it borders on infrared, and at the blue end it borders on ultraviolet. If both ends of the spectrum are joined together, as for example in Goethe's theory of color,[23] this combination, or "unio mystica," will take place at the octave frequency of the Platonic year, resulting in the color violet. In ancient China, "F" was the fundamental tone, or concert pitch, and was known as the "tone of the yellow bell."

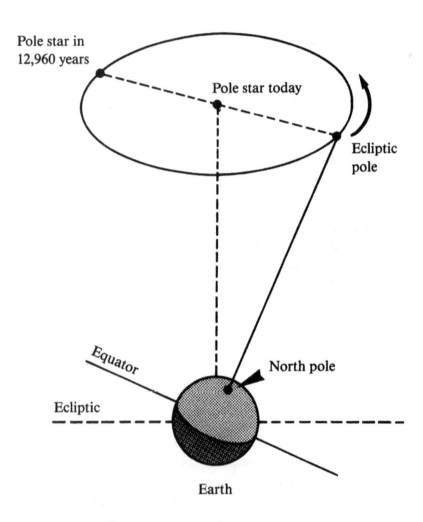

Figure 26. **The gyration of the earth's axis**
The Platonic Year is the length of time the axis of the earth needs to describe a full circle.

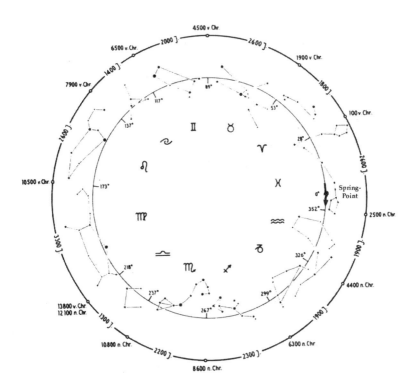

Figure 27. **The journey of the vernal equinox**

The transition of the vernal equinox from one sign of the zodiac to another is indicated in the inner circle by degrees, while the point of the outer circle indicates the approximate date this occurred or will occur. The figures written within the outer circle indicate the length of time the vernal equinox took or will take to pass from one sign to the next. [5] (same as note 5 in chpt. 1)

Yellow is complementary to violet. The reason why the tone was named after the complementary color can be explained by the Taoist idea of polarity, Yin and Yang. In ancient China, great importance was attached to the fundamental tone and to all other basic systems of measurement, as the following passage from *Li Gi, The Book of Customs* proves:

> Thus one must examine the sounds to understand the tones; one must examine the tones to understand the music; one must examine the music to understand the laws. In this way, the path to order is made perfect. Once cannot talk about tones to those who do not understand the sounds. One cannot talk about music to those who do not understand the tones. He who understands music will thus penetrate the secrets of the customs. He who has experienced both customs and music possesses life. Life is experience. [24]

Just as "G," the tone of an earth day, has a dynamic effect on physical processes and "C sharp" will calm and relax the soul, the tone of the Platonic year has a clarifying and cheering effect on the spirit. "G" is indicated in Europe and America by a treble "G," and is a central note in Western music. Accordingly, a lot of attention is paid to physical, material things in the West. The hobbyhorse of Western science is the study of things, and the main precept of Western medicine is to preserve life. Western doctors are obliged to keep a body alive as long as technically possible, even when the person involved is unconscious or no longer wishes to live. The heart and circulation must be kept functioning, and as long as this is the case, the person is said to be alive. In most countries, doctors are not allowed to provide patients a pleasant and pain-free death. Indeed, were they to do so, they would be prosecuted.

In India, however, the situation is very different, since death is not regarded as the end but as a transition of the soul to a new incarnation. The soul was of prime importance in the religious life of ancient Indian society. In accordance, the tone of an earth year was chosen to be the fundamental tone. Indian meditation music, always played in "C sharp," stimulates the soul and makes it resonate. On the other hand, in ancient China more emphasis was laid on the spirit. The transfiguration of the spirit has always been a central theme of Far Eastern wisdom, both in Taoism and Confucianism. These teachings are always told with a certain degree of wit and humor, and wit will tell you a lot about the wits, or spirit of a person, for humorless people are not witty, i.e., they are not clear in spirit. The spirit is the "highest" level of man, and is "above" the body and the soul. The spirit is a continuum, and is not affected by the emotionalism of the soul. John Lilly, the American psychiatrist well-known for his research with dolphins, names the goal of meditation as "sublime indifference."[25] I find this a very apt way of expressing a view of life rooted in the depths of the spirit, beyond all "good" and "bad."

The Chinese emphasis on spirit has to do undoubtedly with the fact that their concert pitch was the tone "F." In no other culture, including that of ancient Greece, where the so-called Pythagorean teachings and traditions came very close to the Chinese teachings of the "middle way," was the meaning of music so important for spiritual and cultural life as was true in China.

Timothy Leary, the well-known American professor and one of the greatest teachers of wisdom of the 20th century, experienced enlightenment while having a shower. He summarized what took place with the six words, "TURN ON, TUNE IN, DROP OUT." When Leary began to emphasize the process of transformation in society at a later point, this slogan proved very useful. In his autobiography, *Know What You Do,* [26] he wrote:

> *Turn on* means to go within and activate your neural and genetic equipment. It means to become receptive for the many and various levels of consciousness and to become aware of the special lever for waking them. Drugs are only *one* way of attaining this goal.
>
> *Tune in* means to integrate harmoniously with your environment and relate to it, to introduce and realize new perspectives.

Drop out indicates an active, selective and graceful process of departure from involuntary or unconscious duties. It means to rely on oneself and to discover that you are a unique person; to follow a path of mobility, selection and change.

"I'm on" is active and corresponds to the "G," the tone of an earth day. "Tune in," on the other hand, corresponds to "C sharp," the tone of an earth year, which helps achieve harmony on the level of the soul. This is the stage of "sublime indifference," a state which is beyond the emotions of the soul. "Drop out" corresponds to "F," the tone of the Platonic year. If these remarks seem farfetched, I recommend reading Timothy Leary, John Lilly, Walter Clark and Robert Anton Wilson. These authors, who all investigate different areas of consciousness, know and collaborate with each other. Aside from Walter Clark, I have met them all and learned a lot about consciousness and self-perception in the process. Leary studied the teachings of the Far East very closely, and wrote commentaries on and interpretations of the *Tibetan Book of the Dead* (Bardo Thodol) and that great book of Chinese wisdom, the *I Ching, the Book of Changes.* His comments on the latter are found in his book *Play of Life,*[27] which he wrote in prison. Leary was sentenced to over 20 years' imprisonment for possession of a few ounces of cannabis. The *I Ching, the Book of Changes,* was also written in prison, as Richard Wilhelm states in his introduction to the same:

According to general tradition, which we have no reason to challenge, the present collection of sixty-four hexagrams originated with King Wen, progenitor of the Chou dynasty. He is said to have added brief judgments to the hexagrams during his imprisonment at the hands of the tyrant Chou Hsin. The text pertaining to the individual lines originated with his son. [28]

The *I Ching* is a book of Chinese wisdom; indeed, it is *the* book of Chinese wisdom. Once again I quote Richard Wilhelm:

In its judgment, and in the interpretations attached to it from the time of Confucius on, the *Book of Changes* opens to the reader the richest treasure of Chinese wisdom; at the same time, it affords him a comprehensive view of the varieties of human experience, enabling him thereby to shape his life of his own sovereign will into an organic whole and so to direct it that it comes into accord with the ultimate Tao lying at the root of all that exists. [29]

The Word of the Christians and the Jews (. . .and God spoke. . .) and the "Nada," "Brahman," and "Atman" (the primordial tone or frequency) of the Hindus, is the "innermost meaning" of the Chinese, the same meaning that Hermann Hesse wrote about in his *Glass Bead Game:*

> Whether you now become a teacher, scholar or musician, you should respect the "innermost meaning," but not consider that it can be taught. [30]

The goal of education in ancient China was to achieve unity with this meaning, which stands above all else. The path to this meaning is Tao. Tao is the path of life and the path of all things. In ancient China, education was based on music, music which was "in accordance with the laws of nature." The Chinese, who had the widest of horizons, chose the great rhythm of the earth, the "F," the tone of the Platonic year, to be their fundamental tone. This is the origin and source of the great wisdom of ancient China.

The Tone of the Platonic Year in Everyday Life

The tone of the Platonic year is associated with cheerfulness, a cheerfulness beyond both suffering and desire. It corresponds to the highest chakra, the sahasrara chakra, which is found on the crown of the skull. To once again quote Hans David:

> The sahasrara chakra represents the highest stage of spiritual development. It is the stage where all the problems, conflicts and tensions of life have been resolved or overcome and transcended. Man is now able to

make full use of his potential. When the kundalini opens up this chakra, with its boundless realms, the yogi experiences a final state of unity–samadhi. This highest level of realization is not affected by temporal limitation. [31]

The corresponding acupuncture point lies on the Du-mai, or Governor Vessel, next to the fontanel on the skull. The fontanel is a membrane-covered opening in the skull which grows together after babyhood. In most acupuncture tables, this point is number 20. The "G" and "C sharp" tuning forks should be applied to this point before "F," otherwise the "F" vibration will not be experienced and appreciated fully.

Should a vibration ever reverberate too strongly, the antidote is to apply another, generally a higher one. If the day tone, "G," becomes uncomfortable, for example, it can be counterbalanced by the year tone, "C sharp," which in turn can be offset by "F." In all the years that I have worked with these tones, I have never met anyone who had any problems at all with "F."

The day tone, "G," is a tone for the young and for people who want children, since it is dynamic in effect, while the year tone, "C sharp," is more suitable for helping people see though the mid-life crisis with its calming and fortifying qualities. The "F" of the Platonic year is mainly for the old and the wise, for those who have lived out their physical needs and who have discovered the wisdom that comes with age. In this context, the terms "young" and "old" have nothing to do with age. I know sixteen-year-old boys who are wiser than most sixty-year-olds, but I also know gentlemen over sixty who do not seem old at all.

Sun   ☉
Earth ☊
Moon   ☽

At new moon the sun is in conjunction with the moon   ☉ ☌ ☽

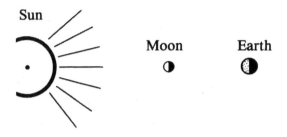

At full moon the sun is in opposition to the moon.   ☉ ☍ ☽

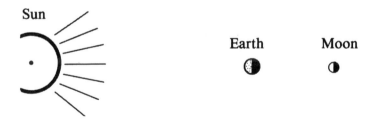

Figure 28. **The new moon and the full moon**
    When the moon is between the sun and the earth, it takes on the appearance of a new moon. However, when the earth passes between the sun and the moon, the latter appears full.

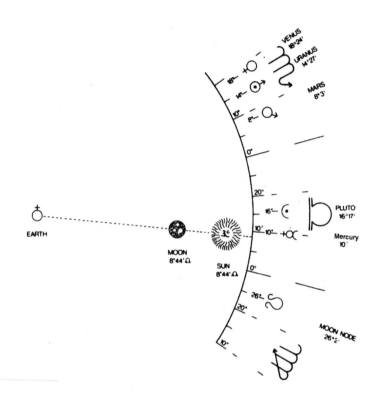

Figure 29. The Position of the new moon

On October 2, 1978, at 6:41 a.m. Greenwich Mean Time, there was a conjunction of the sun and moon at 8 degrees 44' in Libra. In other words, there was a new moon. Mercury was almost in conjunction with the sun and the moon. At 8:47 p.m. Greenwich Mean Time on the same day, a Moon-Pluto conjunction took place. The next time the moon passed this point, it was in the early afternoon of October 29, in the same year. However, the sun had wandered into the sign of Scorpio in the meantime, meaning that the moon had to move on through the ecliptic for another 2 ¹/₄ days before catching up with the sun again.[32]

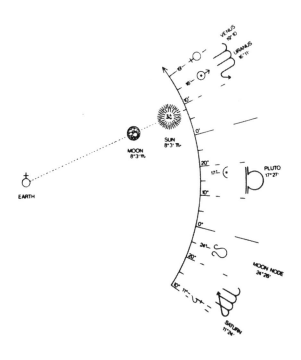

Figure 30. The position of the following new moon

At 8:07 p.m., October 31, 1978, the sun and moon were once again in conjunction, this time at 8 degrees 3' Scorpio. The Moon had traveled through 13 signs of the zodiac before catching up with the sun.

In a tropical and sidereal month, the moon passes through twelve signs of the zodiac, but in a synodic month it travels through thirteen. The synodic month is the length of time from one new moon to another and comprises approximately 29 $\frac{1}{2}$ days. Originally, a month was always of this length, as proved by the designation of "month," which is derived from the word "moon."

CHAPTER 6
THE FREQUENCY OF THE MOON

Corresponding to the Principle of Communication and the Erotic Principle

The moon has several frequencies, each having a different effect. Only the most striking of these will be dealt with here: the frequency of the length of time that passes from one full moon to another–in other words, the frequency of a synodic month. Even the most un-practiced of stargazers will be familiar with the full moon. The wave-length of the synodic month can be heard in the 29th octave (210.42 hertz) and in the 30th (420.84 hertz). In the present-day system of notation, this frequency corresponds to a "G sharp." The corresponding color is bright orange. Orange consists of red and yellow; red stands for will power and yellow for an attitude of expectancy or anticipation. Orange is an instinctual and dynamic color.

The Moon, Health and Sexuality

At full moon, the sun and moon are at opposite sides of the earth, while at new moon, they are both on the same side. Since the power of the sun and moon are combined at new moon, it is a time of con-centrated energy. This is quite the opposite case at full moon, when the sun and moon exert their respective influences from different sides of the earth. This is the time of greatest polarity, the time when Yin and Yang are in opposition, the time with the greatest potential for tension. The way people behave at full moon reflects this state of po-larity, when opposites are striving for unity.

The moon also has a lot to do with sexuality. The word menstrua-tion, for example, is derived from "mensis," Latin for month. Both the menstruation and fertility are influenced by the moon. The full moon draws people together and it is the best time for conception. Making use of this knowledge as a means of natural birth control is known as lunaception.

The moon influences sexuality and its accompanying emotions. Tuning forks representing the tone of the moon, or music written in this key, can be used to support the treatment of menstruation problems; lunaception, for example, has been in successful use for several years. In the same way that the moon influences the ebb and flow of tides, it also affects the balance of bodily fluids, and disturbances due to an imbalance of these fluids can be treated with the "G sharp" moon tuning fork.

In medical circles, the method of treating certain acupuncture points with vibrations is known as "phonophorese," an area of medicine in which the French doctor Jean Lamy has proved to be outstanding. [33]

Here is a list of the points that have proved most useful in the treatment of the sexual organs. The list is doubtlessly incomplete and should simply encourage you to feel and experience the flow of energy in the meridians for yourself. The phonophorese method is extremely easy and not at all dangerous, unlike acupuncture with needles or moxabustion, a method of treatment in which a wad of moxa, usually made of a Chinese kind of mugwort (*Artemisia vulgaris var. sinensis*) is held over the acupuncture points, which are protected from overheating by a thin slice of garlic or ginger. Both techniques have been used in China for thousands of years. The oldest technique of all is probably acupressure, the method of massaging acupuncture points.

Favorable points are, among others, point 1 on the pericardium meridian, located two fingers away from the nipples on the chest at the level of the fourth and fifth ribs (from the neck down). In the case of well-developed breasts, the point will be positioned at the outer edge of the chest, exactly opposite the nipples (see Figure 31 on page 80). This meridian plays an important role in reproduction and has to do with desire and joy.

Two points on the liver meridian also have a very strong influence

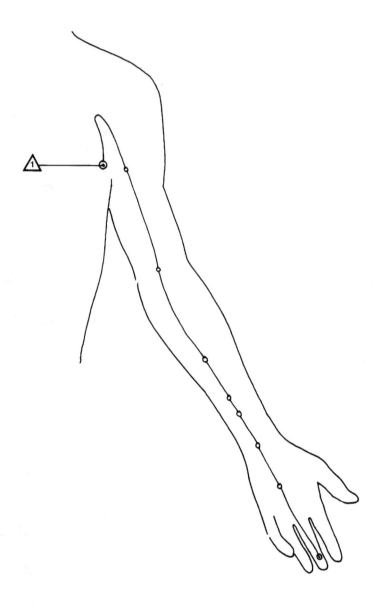

Figure 31. **Illustration of the pericardium meridian, showing point 1**

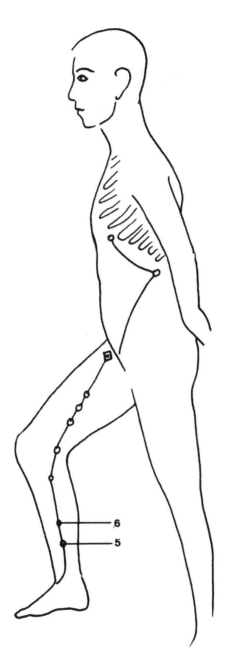

Figure 32. **Illustration of the liver meridian, showing points 5 and 6**

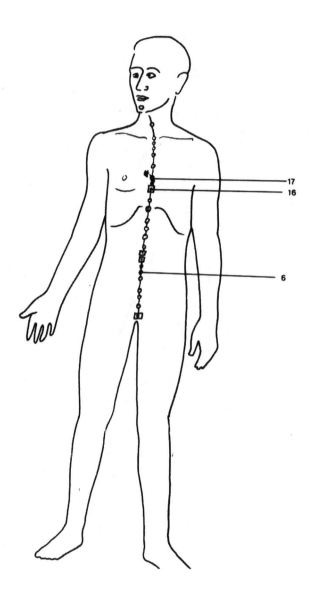

Figure 33. **Illustration of the Ren-mai meridian, showing points 6 and 17**

on the menstruation cycle and can, when activated with a tuning fork, help relieve menstruation problems. The points 5 and 6 are found almost exactly in the middle of the calves on both legs (see Figure 32 on page 81).

There are also a few points on the Ren-mai, or Conception Vessel, that have a regulative effect on the sexual organs of both women and men. Point 6 is found one half inch below the navel and is known as the "sea of energy" or "hara." Another point is 17, positioned on the breastbone (see Figure 33 on page 82), which is regarded as being the most important point on this meridian. If you want to increase the potential of the sexual organs, the best time to treat these points is during full moon. Generally speaking, 10 or 15 minutes are usually sufficient for this treatment, but you can also go by feeling.

I would like to point out that the therapeutic value of tuning fork treatment cannot replace medical treatment. All serious complaints should be treated by a doctor or by a licensed health practitioner. Some doctors are familiar with tuning fork therapy and will include it in the general treatment of a case.

Should you experience any unpleasant sensations when using the tuning forks on yourself, it is a sign that something is wrong. When treating a meridian, the energy in it increases and becomes more sensitive. As a result, you may begin to feel that the energy in the respective organ is stagnant or disordered. Therefore, tuning fork treatment can help determine the presence of energetic or organic disturbances at an early stage. In this respect, someone who has a high degree of bodily awareness will find it easier to judge the effects of tuning fork treatment than those with very little awareness of their body.

Full Moon Festivities

In an earlier age, the calendar was based on the movements of the moon. A Sunday was always on a new moon, a full moon, and a half moon. There were additional holidays (feast days), once or twice a month, usually at the time of the full moon, to coordinate the length of the week with the course of the moon. A Monday (or Moon-day), was always the day when the moon entered a new phase. Thus, in the old days, feast days were in unity with the passage of the moon.

In this day and age, many people have to work during the full moon, which can lead to many accidents. Therefore, I advise all those who do not need to work at this time to desist from doing so and to celebrate and have a good time instead.

In the ancient cultures, the knowledge of procreation determined the dates of the feast days. The Indians celebrate the Holi festival in the month of Caitra, on the same day that the Jews celebrate the Passover. The Passover always takes place on the 14th day of the month of Nisan. This is the first full moon after the beginning of spring, in March or April. At this point the sun is in Aries and the moon in Libra. The most important Christian feast day, the Resurrection (Easter), is always celebrated when the moon is waning, whether by the Roman Catholics, the Protestants, or the reform churches. This is because the Council of Nicaea decreed in the year 325 that Easter was to be celebrated on the first Sunday after the spring full moon (in other words, on the first Sunday after March 21). Therefore, if there is a full moon on March 20, Easter takes place at the end of April, a whole month later.

The Council of Nicaea also decreed that if the spring full moon was to fall on a Sunday, Easter was to be postponed for a week so that the Christians would not have to celebrate Easter on the same day that the Jews celebrated Passover. This ruling has remained to the present day. For all those with eyes to see, it is obvious that the official Church is no longer in unity with the flow of life.

Due to this ruling by the Council of Nicaea, the most important Christian feast day, Easter, is celebrated when the moon is on the wane. From an astrological point of view, this is the time when sexual and vital energies are reaching their lowest point. Since the rhythms of nature remain unaffected by decrees, this ruling has led to the stipulation of celibacy for nuns and priests. Since Catholic clergymen and nuns are forbidden to marry and conceive children, they are unable to participate in the most beautiful ritual of all, the life-giving feast of love.

Sexual restriction generally leads to various forms of vicarious gratification, some of them cruel and abhorrent, as in the case of the Inquisition. The Church has departed a long way from the Biblical commandments of "Be fruitful and multiply" and "Thou shall not kill." The Inquisition serves as a warning of what can happen when cosmic laws are disregarded. For this reason, nature is a better guideline for behavior than dogmatic teachings or laws.

Once more, from The Book of Customs:

> Music is the harmony of Heaven and Earth. All things are transformed by harmony and all things are differentiated by their various stages. The creative origin of music is in Heaven and the customs are formed in accordance with the Earth. When forms become too numerous, confusion occurs. When there is too much creativity, violence occurs. Only when one becomes aware of Heaven and Earth will customs and music come to fruition [34]

CHAPTER 7
THE FREQUENCY OF THE SUN

The Magical, Transcendental Principle

The original frequency of the sun is 32,312.52 hertz, and for this reason it is not necessary to raise it any octaves higher, but to lower it. The first lower octave of the sun, which has only a little more than 16 kilocycles per second, lies within the range of audible sound. The 7th lower octave (of 252.44 hertz) lies within the medium musical range, as does the 8th with 126.22 hertz. The color corresponding to the tone of the sun is a light green.

The tone of the sun is the tone of the 20th century, since it reflects modern quantum physics, both in theory and practice. The tones of the earth, the moon and the other planets are more on the level of the 17th and 18th centuries, since they are analogous to phenomena which can be directly observed and experienced. Apart from the tone of the sun, all the cosmic tones are derived by taking a natural frequency a few octaves higher until it becomes audible. These tones correlate to actual vibrations and natural occurrences. The sun tone, however, is based on pure theory.

This is also the case with absolute zero temperature, which theoretically exists and can be precisely calculated, but does not occur in nature. Moreover, it cannot be brought about artificially because a tremendous amount of energy would be needed to cool matter down to this level. Theoretically speaking, however, there is such a thing as an absolute null temperature.

The tone of the sun is based on a limit value in our solar system that is exactly at the threshold between contraction and expansion, Yin and Yang. Were a planet to have the same oscillation as the sun tone, it would become one with it. Before dealing with the scientific basis of the sun tone in depth, I would like to mention a few fundamental thoughts with regard to scientific research. For example, most people know that Johannes Kepler discovered three natural laws concerning the planets. (These are known as Kepler's laws.) However, few people are aware of how he made these discoveries. From a philosophical point of view, Kepler's achievement was of great significance because he depicted natural laws in mathematical form for the first time.

Johannes Kepler's findings were milestones in the history of natural science, not only because of his discoveries, but also because of the way he observed and investigated certain correlations. In his books, he described how he arrived at his conclusions in such depth that even the modern-day reader can recognize his criteria and reconstruct his approach. Since the calculation of the sun tone occurred to me while reading Kepler's *World Harmony*,[35] and since the scientific basis of this tone is rooted in Kepler's work, it is worthwhile dealing with the personality of Kepler and his work in order to understand this discovery.

Many people believe that Kepler was a physicist and an astronomer. This he certainly was, but he also studied theology at Tübingen University in the Württemberg district of Germany. His teachers did not consider him suitable for doing clerical work in Württemberg, however, mainly because of his divergent approach to Holy Communion. Before finishing his studies, he was invited to teach mathematics at the Lutheran High School in Graz, Austria. It was here in 1596 that he published his *Mysterium Cosmographicum*,[36] his first treatise about the arrangement of the planets, and it was here that he compared the regular platonic bodies with the distances of the planets from the sun.

In 1600, Kepler was invited to Prague by Tycho von Brahe, the Imperial Court Astronomer. Until von Brahe's death in 1601, Kepler worked as his assistant; later, he was appointed court astronomer and mathematician by Rudolph II, who was the King of Bohemia and Hungary and Holy Roman Emperor. In the field of mathematics, Kepler mainly occupied himself with the laws of geometrical figures and with calculating the volume of wine barrels. However, he also turned his attention to music theory, harmonics and astrology, a fact of fundamental importance for the comprehension of the *World Harmonics*. Kepler's study of harmonic relationships in geometry and music led to his astronomical discoveries and to the development of his personal philosophy of life. The five volumes of the *World Harmonics* reflect the path of development that led to the discovery of Kepler's third law of planetary motion. The first two books deal with geometry. The first is titled *"Geometrical* book. Origin and description of the regular figures responsible for harmonic proportions," while the second is called *"Architectonic* book, or book based on the *Geometry of Figures*. Congruency of regular figures in plane and spatial geometry." Volume III, titled "The actual *harmonic* book. Origin of the harmonic proportions of figures. Nature of and difference in musical things, in contrast to the old," is concerned with the interval in music, and includes papers on the number and arrangement of the smallest intervals, the division of the monochord, perfect and imperfect consonants, and various theories about the division of the octave into intervals.

Volume IV, titled *"Metaphysical, psychological and astrological* book. The spiritual form of the different kinds of harmonies in the world. Description of the harmony of rays which shine down on the earth from heavenly bodies and the effect they have on nature or the sublunar soul and on the human soul," deals with the relationships between astrological aspects and musical intervals. In Volume V, which is titled, *"Astronomical* and *metaphysical* book. The most perfect harmonies of the movements of the planets and the origin of eccentricities in the harmonic proportions," he introduces the foundations of his third law of planetary motion. An appendix in *World Harmonics* contains "a comparison of this work with the 3rd book of harmonics written by Claudius Ptolemy and the observations on harmony made by Robertus de Fluctibus, named Fludd, doctor in Oxford, in his book about the macrocosm and the microcosm."

Kepler's second law of planetary motion states that the radius vector from the sun to each planet generates equal orbital areas in equal times. Representing a certain period of time is "t," while "F" represents the area passed in this period.

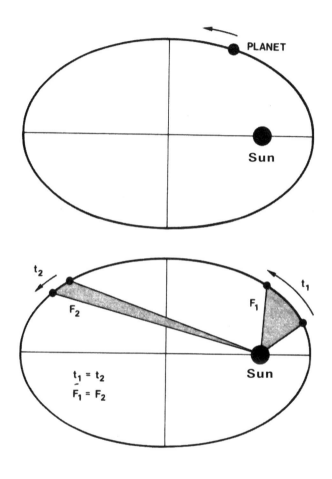

Figure 34. Kepler's First Law of Planetary Motion (upper diagram)
Kepler's Second Law of Planetary Motion (lower diagram)

The Discovery of the Sun Tone

The discovery of the sun tone was nothing other than the logical consequence of Figure 35, which shows a log-log graph of the solar system. The horizontal axis shows the orbits of the planets in seconds. The left vertical axis displays the mean distance of the planets from the sun, while the right one portrays the orbital speed in kilometers per second. If the planets on this graph are connected together, the result will be a straight line, clearly expressing the inherent order of our solar system. Of course, this kind of order not only applies to the solar system, but is also present in all similar systems.

The straight line represents a function existent between orbit, orbital speed, and mean distance from the sun. Kepler formulated this function in his third law of planetary motion, which states that the ratio of the square of the revolution period to the cube of the major orbital axis is the same for all the planets.

Since Mercury is the closest planet to the sun, the straight line in the graph begins with Mercury and ends with Pluto, which, according to present-day knowledge, is the planet furthest away from the sun. Theoretically, other planets could still be discovered, in which case our straight line would have to be lengthened.

It was the "origin" of this straight line which made me think; I wanted to find out where the limit would be if a similar situation were depicted in such a graph. A limit in orbital speed seemed likely, for there is an absolute top speed—namely the speed of light. My task was now to discover how long it would take a planet moving at the speed of light to orbit the sun, and how great its mean distance to the sun would be.

It would be beyond the scope of this book to include the necessary calculations, and these in turn would demand a certain grasp of mathematics on the part of the reader. Those interested in the exact derivation and calculation of the sun tone are referred to my book *Die Kosmische Oktave–Der Weg zum universellen Einklang.*[37] Here I will restrict myself to the results of these calculations and a comparison of the planetary orbits.

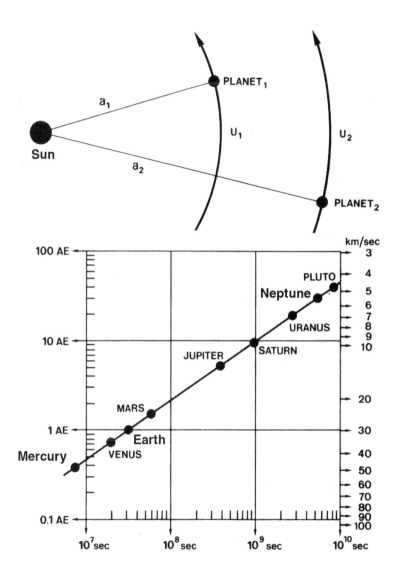

Figure 35. **Kepler's Third Law of Planear Motion (above)**
The above illustration demonstrate Kepler's third law of planetary motion and the law of gravity. Below: a graph of the solar system on log-log paper. [38]

Orbital data of our theoretical planet

Orbital speed = speed of light: 299,792.5 km/sec
Mean distance to the sun: 1,476,625 km
Period of revolution around the sun: 0.030,95 sec
Frequency of the period of revolution: 32,312.52 hertz

Mercury is the planet closest to the sun. Of all the planets, it has the fastest orbit, the shortest period of revolution and the smallest mean distance. Pluto, on the other hand, is the planet farthest away from the sun. Correspondingly, it has the slowest orbit, the longest period of revolution and the greatest mean distance. The following table is a comparison of the data of the orbits of Mercury and Pluto:

PLANET	MERCURY	Factor/Difference(*)	PLUTO
Speed of orbit:	47 km/sec	0.1	4.7 km/sec
Audible Frequency:	141.27 hz	1	140.25 hz
Octave Number:	30	10*	40
Distance from the sun in asronomical units:	0.39 A.U.	100	39 A.U.
Period of revolution:	.25 years	1,000	250 ears

The closer a planet is to the sun, the greater its speed of orbit; in other words, the period of revolution and the mean distance to the sun become shorter and shorter. Our theoretical planet races around the sun at the speed of light, 300,000 km per second. The speed of this orbit is 6,000 times faster than that of Mercury and 60,000 times faster than that of Pluto. In other words, its mean distance (1.476 kilometers) is 40 million times smaller than that of Mercury and four billion (4,000,000,000) times smaller than that of Pluto. The period of revolution, consisting of 0.000,03 seconds, would then be 250 billion times smaller than that of Mercury, and 250 trillion times smaller than that of Pluto.

These are gigantic figures that are difficult to imagine. However, if the respective tones are compared to each other in octaves, the whole business takes on manageable proportions. The sun tone of 32,312.52 hertz (the original frequency) is about 38 octaves higher than the tone of Mercury and about 48 octaves higher than that of Pluto. A piano consists of a little over 7 octaves. It is much easier to imagine a few keyboards lined up than several hundred billion. This is the advantage of imagining certain relations in octave form, for huge dimensions can be reduced to manageable form. This is known as a logarithmic procedure, while the numerical approach is directly proportional to the quantity in question.

The hypothesis of a planet racing around the sun at the speed of light has a lot to do with the "being" of our "world," for it demonstrates that the existence of completely different worlds is not so very improbable. The distance of our theoretical planet to the center of the sun would correspond exactly to the gravitational length of the sun. This term denotes the radius of a mass possessing surface forces of attraction so great that nothing can be released from this mass, neither electrons nor photons. Such concentrations are called black holes.

The surface of a black hole has such a high degree of attractive power that the speed a particle would need to leave it would have to be faster than the speed of light. For this reason, black holes radiate neither light nor electromagnetic waves. Instead, they attract everything that comes close to them. It has not yet been possible to observe the conditions that exist in the interior of a black hole. Were the mass of the earth to be compressed to a small black hole, it would fit into a thimble. Its diameter would be smaller than a centimeter and the whole solar system would be a ball about three kilometers in diameter. There are parts of the universe no larger than a few kilometers, yet they are as "heavy" as our solar system. These parts are black holes. The conditions that exist in a black hole are totally disparate from those in the world as we know it.

The sun tone corresponds to the limits of physical existence. The world beyond this frequency is completely different from ours. It is a world with other dimensions, other concepts of space and time, a world existing beyond Einstein's theory of relativity. In order to imagine this new world, it is necessary to transcend all you have ever heard and seen and become open for completely new "fantasies" and "images."

As John Wheeler, one of the best-known scientists of our time, said at the relativity conference in Oxford, on February 16, 1974:

> Perhaps there is no such thing as a glittering mechanism in the center of the universe. . . Maybe we should think of the treasure that is waiting for us there more in terms of magic than as a mechanism. [39]

The sun tone represents a door from one world into another. It is the exit from the known, mechanistic and physical world, and the entrance to a new world—a magic world.

If you hear it when you are tense, a thrill will run through you and make you shudder. For many people, this tone is strange and uncanny, for some it is threatening. Therefore, it would be better to experiment with the tones of the earth, the moon and the planets before trying out the sun tone.

Children learn to walk at home and in familiar surroundings. It is only when they can walk with a certain degree of ability that they begin to roam farther afield. For the same reason, it is advisable to first attune yourself to the vibrations more closely connected to your life, such as those of the earth and the moon. Once you have become more sensitized and are able to resonate in unity with certain basic vibrations, you can leave familiar dimensions without damage to yourself and step over the threshold of Yin and Yang.

Meditation music attuned to this tone is beyond all imagination and will lead the listener into new dimensions. Above all, it is recommended for people whose souls are full of joy and whose spirits are clear, for those who are prepared to leave everything they know behind them, without regret. Meditation carried out to this tone will lead the listener to a state beyond good and bad, shame and guilt, beyond space and time, knowledge and wisdom, action and rest, and being and non-being. It leads to a state where being has no name, to a state where the all-one and the all-encompassing are no longer separate entities but are reunited at their one, common origin, the origin that is also you.

Notes

Preface
1. *Li Gi, Das Buch der Sitte.* Düsselfodrf/Cologne, W. Germany: Eugen Diedrichs Verlag, p. 68.
2. *Li Gi*, p. 76.
3. Hesse, Hermann, *Magister Ludi* (The Glass Bead Game). USA: Henry Holt & Co. Ltd., 1949.
4. Cousto, *Relating Sound to Color and the Cosmic Octave.* Vol. I, author's edition, Munich, 1997.
5. Cousto, *Die kosmische Oktave.* Essen: Synthesis Verlag, 1984.
6. Cousto, *Relating Sound to Color and the Cosmic Octave.* Vol. II, author's edition, Mainz, 1982.

Chapter 1
7. *Li Gi.* p. 15.

Chapter 2
8. Baumer, Metz and Eichmer, *Die Atmoshperics-Aktivität bei 10 und 27 kHz als Indikator für die Dynamik der troposhpärischen Wettervorgänge.* Archives for Meteorology, geophysics and bioclimatology, Ser. B 29 (1981), p. 299 f.
9. Baumer, Hans, *Die Meteorotrophie eines Dichromat-Gelatinesystems.* Technischer Informationsdienst, Abteilung Technik und Forschung, Fachbereich Tiefdruck, Bundesverbady Druck I, 1982, p. 13.
10. Krüger, Willfried, *Das Universum singt.* Editions Treves, 1982, pp. 63, 67.

Chapter 3
11. Lüscher, Max *Der klinishe Lüschertest.*
12. David, Hans, *Die Welt des Yoga.* Berlin: Alpha Verlag, 1986, p. 237.
13. David, Hans, *Die Welt des Yoga.* Berlin: Alpha Verlag, 1986, p. 238.

Chapter 4
14. Cousto, *Musik im Einklang mit der Erde.* Einblick, 4/1986, Berlin.
15. Lilly, John, *The Center of the Cyclone; an Autobiography of Inner Space.* New York, Crown Publishers, 1985.
16. Lilly, John, *der Scientist.* Basel: Sphinx Verlag, 1984.

17. Lilly, John, *Simulationen von Gott.* Basel: Sphinx Verlag, 1986.
18. Sheldrake, Rupert, *New Science of Life; Hypothesis of Formative Causation.* Los Angeles: J. Tarcher, 1981.
19. Jung, Carl Gustav, *Collected Works.*
20. Vetter, Michael, *Overtones/Tambura-Meditationen.* Freiburg, West Germany: Hermann bauer verlag.
21. Vetter, Michael, *Obertonmesse (MIssa Universalis).* Freiburg, West Germany: Hermann bauer verlag.
22. Wolff, Stephanie, *Obertöne.* cassette with accompanying booklet, Freiburg, West Germany: Hermann Bauer Verlag, 1984.

Chapter 5
23. Goethe, Johann Wolfgang von, *Farbelehre.*
24. *Li Gi, Das Buch der Sitte.* Eugen Diederichs Verlag Düsseldorf/Cologne, W. Germany, p. 73.
25. Lilly, John, Simulationen von Gott.
26. Leary, Timothy, *Know What you Do.* Basel: Sphinx Verlag, 1986.
27. Leary, Timothy, *Man of Life.* Basel: Sphinx Verlag, 1982.
28. Wilhem, Richard, *I Ching.* Routledge & Kegan Paul Ltd., London, 1951, p. lix.
29. *Ibid.* p. lvii.
30. Hesse, Hermann, *Magister Ludi, The Glass Bead Game.* New York, bantam Books, 1970.

Chapter 6
31. David, Hans, *Die Welt des Yoga.* Berlin: Alpha Verlag, 1986, p. 243.
32. Cousto, *Relating Sound to Color.* vol. I.
33. Lamy, Jean, *Ursprung des Lebens.* Essen: Verlag für Ganzheitsmedizin, 1984.
34. *Li Gi.* p. 76.

Chapter 7
35. Kepler, Johannes, *Weltharmonik.* Linz, 1619, Beck, München, 1938.
36. Johannes, *Mysterium cosmographicum.* Graz, 1596.
37. Cousto, *Die kosmische Oktave.* Essen: Synthesis Verlag, 1984, p. 209 ff.
38. Cousto, *Die kosmische Oktave.* Essen: Synthesis Verlag, 1984, p. 209 ff.
39. Toben, Bob, *Space, Time and Beyond.* New York, Dutton, 1975.

THE COSMIC OCTAVE TUNING FORKS

LifeRhythm sells steel tuning forks created to Cousto's specifications. They are tuned by hand and calibrated at 20 degrees C. to each planet, the moon and sun, corresponding to color and sound. By tuning into the sound and color of your aura, chakras and internal processes, you can revitalize and enhance your whole energy system. Meditate and chant the sounds of the planets, activate acupressure points—unfold with unlimited cosmic creativity.

Planets	Frequency	Earth Tones	Frequency
Mercury	141.27	Sidereal Day	194.71
Venus	221.23	Platonic Year	172.06
Mars	144.72	Earth Year OM	136.10
Jupiter	183.58		
Saturn	147.85	**Moon Tones**	**Frequency**
Uranus	207.36	Synoptic Moon	210.42
Neptune	211.44	Sidereal Moon	227.43
Pluto	140.25		
		Sun	126.22
		Mid-Sun	194.18

**These tuning forks can be ordered from our website
or by telephone or fax.**

LifeRhythm
P.O. Box 806, Mendocino CA 95460 USA
(707) 937-1825 Fax: (707) 937-3052
Email: books@LifeRhythm.com
website: www.LifeRhythm.com

APPENDIX I

PREFACE

the autumn of 1979, the "interplanetarian" tuning forks and their frequencies became more and more a topic of *m*versation; a lot of people wanted to learn about these cosmic vibrations so that it became impossible to answer these questions directly person to person. The necessity arose to put down some essential thoughts and *n*damental calculations in booklet form, to give interested circles at least some kind of frame of reference for *'i*r own thoughts on this subject.

*ri*ng the Moon-Pluto conjunction on 2. October 1978, the first sound frequencies of the Earth's movement *re* calculated according to the law of the octave. After precisely 13 more Moon-Pluto conjunctions, on Saturday, . October 1979, a first informational booklet entitled "FARBTON – TONFARBE UND DIE KOSMISCHE *K*TAVE" had been put together, containing the 3 tones of the Earth (the »G« of the day, the »C sharp« of *'* year, the platonic »F«) and the tone of Venus (the »Venus-A«). At the following Moon-Pluto conjunction, Friday, 16. November 1979, the tones of the sidereal revolutions of all planets were presented in form of *a*ing forks and a second booklet, in which, in addition to the tones of the planets, also the two basic tones of the *o*on (synodic and sidereal) were discussed. On Friday, 14. December 1979, there was another Moon-Pluto *a*junction, and the third booklet, an extended summary of the first two editions, had been published, since these *re* already out of print.

*i*s fourth version has been substantially extended and contains all texts and formulas of the first three editions. *n*y answers to questions asked by readers of the earlier booklets have been integrated into this new text. *e* text explains and formalizes all steps necessary to calculate standard pitches (for tuning purposes) from *on*omical data of the planetary motions.

ELATING SOUND TO COLOR
ND THE COSMIC OCTAVE

)edicated to the Players of the Glass Bead Game

The action of a single man brought the Bead Game
lmost instantaneously to a realization of its potentia-
ties, and therewith to the threshold of an universal
tpacity for development. And once again it was the
onjunction with music that caused this progress.
A Swiss music teacher, who was at the same time a
matical lover of mathematics, gave a new twist to
ie game, thus opening the way towards its highest
xpansion. The bourgeois name of this man cannot
e revealed, for in his age the cult of the individual
o longer existed in intellectual circles. (...)
He had invented for the Bead Game the basis of a
ew speech, namely a mixture of symbols and formu-
s in which music and mathematics played an equal
art, and in which it was possible to combine astono-
ical and musical formulas under a common deno-
inator. Even if development remained unrestricted,
ie basis of all the later history of our worthy game
as postulated by this unknown man.«

rom »The Glass Bead Game« by Hermann Hesse

N ASTRONOMICAL, MATHEMATICAL,
USICAL ACCOUNT
F A BLISSFUL VISION

an unknown Swiss music scholar and passionate
athematician, beheld through the 108 pearls of the
ain of harmony which cause our solar-system to
sonate. A few of these pearls are introduced and
plained on the following pages.

TIME, FREQUENCY AND THE OCTAVE

The concept of time gives rise to various associations
in various people. Many people in the Western culture
often have too little of it, and sometimes say: »I don't
have time«, or »I don't have enough time«. This
shows clearly that time does not only refer to the
dimension of experience but – in terms of algebra –
to a certain amount of it. Most people mean a length
of time when they say »time«. The way time is experienced, is conditioned by our consciousness.
For the physicist, it is a basic dimension with a certain direction which is not reversable. For some sages
of the East (Gurus, Yogis) time does not exist as such,
but only as an antipole to that which cannot be
experienced in terms of time. In many cultures this is
called »eternity«.
The concept of time will not be used here in a strictly
analytical, logical, physical sense, but as the duration
of a period of time as it is experienced by most
people.

TIME is not really an independant concept of its
own, but a duration. Throughout history time has
been defined as the period between two certain astronomical constellations (mostly of the same kind). The
period of time from one sun's passage of the upper
culmination (at midday) till the next is called a
»day«. The period from one commencement of spring
till the next is called a year.
Days and years are periodical phenomena, following
one another in regular succession. Time is the period
of oscillation of periodic phenomena.

FREQUENCY (Latin: frequentia) expresses the
number of repetitions of a periodic phenomenon
during a certain length of time. (Vibrations/unit of
time.) Periodic phenomena (for example days, years,
lunar cycles) are vibrations. The measuring unit of
vibrations ist stated in terms of time units. (This
newspaper once had three editions a day, it appeared
three times a day. A tuning fork vibrates at the rate
of 272.2 vibrations per second, vibrating 272.2 times
back and forth in one second.) One vibration per
second is called 1 Hertz (in physical articles the notation »sec^{-1}« is coming more and more into use for »1

Hz (1 Hertz)«. In musical handbooks the term »Hertz« is still being used – the measuring unit of vibrations. The number of a frequency, given in »Hertz«, is the number of oscillations during the period of one second. One second is the equivalent of the 86 400th part of an average day.

OCTAVE (Latin: octava – the eighth) is the eighth step in a diatonic sequence, which is given by the same letter as the initial note.
According to the oldest Greek musical theory of Philolaos, the octave was first called »Harmonia« and later »Diapason«. The division of a string reveals the octave as the simplest proportion (1:2).
In terms of physics the first rising octave is the first overtone of a tonic and has double the frequency. The first descending octave of a tonic has half the frequency of the tonic.
To form an octave is to double a frequency or to halve it.

OCTAVUS SANCTOS OMNES DOCET ESSE BEATOS
»The octave teaches the saints bliss«, reads one of the mysterious inscriptions on the capitels at the abbey church of Cluny.

»Every figure, every row of numbers and every assemblage of harmonious sounds and the accordance of the cycles of the celestial bodies – and the One – as an analogy for all which is manifesting itself – must become exceedingly clear to him who is searching in the right manner. That of which we speak will however come to light if one strives to recognize all, while not loosing sight of the One. It is then that the connecting link of the Ones named will come to light.«   Platon

The length of time a celestial body requires to rotate around its axis and to revolve around the sun can be converted into sound and color by means of the law of the octave. These sounds (and colors) are analogous to that which presents itself in the heavens and on earth.

The formula of which mathematics and music equally partake, enabling one to combine astronomical and musical formulas, a common denominator for astronomy, mathematics, music, even for colors, is the law of the octave.

To form an octave is to double or halve a given frequency.

Thus, of any frequency a_0
the first ascending octave has the frequency
$$a_1 = 2 \cdot a_0 = a_0 \cdot 2^1$$
the second ascending octave has the frequency
$$a_2 = 4 \cdot a_0 = a_0 \cdot 2^2$$
the third ascending octave has the frequency
$$a_3 = 8 \cdot a_0 = a_0 \cdot 2^3$$
the fourth ascending octave has the frequency
$$a_4 = 16 \cdot a_0 = a_0 \cdot 2^4$$
the nth ascending octave has the frequency
$$a_n = a_0 \cdot 2^n$$
the $(n+1)^{th}$ ascending octave has the frequency
$$a_{(n+1)} = 2 \cdot a_n = a_0 \cdot 2^{(n+1)}$$
the twenty-fourth ascending octave has the frequency
$$a_{24} = 16\ 777\ 216 \cdot a_0 = a_0 \cdot 2^{24}$$

The period of oscillation and its frequency stand in a relation of inverse proportionality, thus
$$period = \frac{1}{frequency} \quad and \quad frequency = \frac{1}{period}$$
The reciprocal value of a period of time represents its frequency, for example, the earth takes 365.24 days for its orbit around the sun, thus the corresponding frequency is: $\frac{1}{365.24\ days}$ This frequency is then doubled (multiplied by 2) until the octave notes reach the range of hearing. Having multiplied n-times by 2 the audible frequency is equal to

$$\frac{1}{length\ of\ period} \cdot 2^n = tone\ frequency.$$

Fourty octaves higher one obtains the matching frequency in the visible range. About eight octaves below the average audible frequencies are those frequencies we perceive as tempo, meter (Latin form of the Greek μέτρον, measure), time and rhythm.

Apart from forming the reciprocal value (thereby converting the length of a period into a frequency) and multiplying by the number 2 (thereby forming the next higher octave), no other mathematical knowledge is required to calculate a meter, a note or a color which is analogous to an astronomical period.

THE DAY

The Average Solar Day — The Corresponding Meter

An average solar day has 24 hours, that's $24 \cdot 60 = 1440$ minutes. A day has a duration of 1440 minutes, the period of the 16th octave of the day is $\frac{1440 \ min}{2^{16}} = 0.021\ 973$ minutes, which corresponds to a frequency of: $\frac{2^{16}}{1440 \ min} = \frac{1}{0.021\ 973min} = 45.51$ vibrations per minute.

A meter of 45.51 beats per minute corresponds to the 16th octave of an average solar day, twice that, 91.02 beats per minute, corresponds to the 17th octave, four times 45.51 is 182.04 beats per minute, corresponding to the 18th octave of an average solar day.

The Pendulum Corresponding to the Day

The length of a pendulum is determined by the formula: $l = \frac{T^2 \cdot g}{4\pi^2}$ »l« is the length to be calculated, »T« is the duration of the pendulum's oscillation (back and forth), $g = 9.81 \ m/sec^2 =$ the gravitational acceleration on earth and $\pi = 3.141\ 592\ 653 =$ the proportional number of the diameter and circumference of a circle.

Given: $T = 0.021\ 973 \ min = 1.318\ 360 \ sec$, then: $\frac{(1.318\ 360)^2 sec^2 \cdot 9.81 \ m/sec^2}{4\pi^2} = 0.432 \ m$.

A pendulum of the length of about 43 cm oscillates an octave relationship (as an octave note) to an average solar day.

A pendulum of one fourth, or of four times this length does so as well.

The Note Corresponding to the Day

An average solar day lasts 24 hours, that is 1440 minutes or 86 400 seconds ($24 \cdot 60 \cdot 60$). The 25th octave or the 2^{25}th $= 33\ 554\ 432$th partial note of a solar day is therefore:

$$\frac{1}{86\ 400sec} \cdot 33\ 554\ 432 = 388.36 \ Hz$$

This frequency corresponds approximately to a »G'« (given an »A'« of 435 Hz and temperate tuning). The corresponding chromatic, welltempered »G« has the frequency:

$435 \ Hz \cdot \sqrt[12]{2^{-2}} = 435 \ Hz \cdot 2^{-1/6} =$
$435 \ Hz \cdot 2^{-0.1\overline{6}} = 435 \ Hz \cdot 0.890899 =$
$387.54 \ Hz$

The frequency in the welltempered chromatic tuning system changes from one semitone to the next by the factor $\sqrt[12]{2} = 1.059\ 463$ ($1.059\ 463^{12} = 2$). The difference in frequency between the »G« derived from the day and the chromatic »G« is less than 1 Hz. The matching chromatic »A'« for the note of the day of 388.36 Hz is found at:

$388.36 \cdot \sqrt[12]{2^2} \ Hz = 388.36 \cdot 2^{1/6} \ Hz =$
$388.36 \cdot 2^{0.1\overline{6}} \ Hz = 388.36 \cdot 1,122\ 462 =$
$435.92 \ Hz$

Electronic chromatic tuning machines with a frequency indicator for the note »A'« can be adjusted accordingly. One generates the note »G« and adjusts the indicator to 435.92 Hz and then one hears a »G« of 194.18 Hz, the 24th octave of the average solar day, or 388.36 Hz, the 25th octave of the average solar day. ($194.18 \ Hz \cdot 2 = 388.36 \ Hz$)

The 25th octave of an average solar day is indicated in the European system of musical notation by the treble clef:

In French speaking countries this note is called »sol«. This name was given in the 11th century by the Benedictine monk Guido di Arezzo, who took the first syllable from the fifth measure of the hymn of St. John »Ut queant laxis« by Paulus Diaconus, while, as music teacher of the cathedral school at Arezzo, he named the notes after this hymn to teach them to his students.

To calculate the note »G« or »sol« one uses exclusively the relation of the earth to the sun, both containing the syllable »sol« in French.
Le sol – the earth, the ground.
Le soleil – the sun.
The intonation of notes is called »solfier«. The songbook and notebook one called »solfège«.
The following audible frequencies are all natural overtones of the solar day:

> 24.273 Hz – 21. octave
> 48.545 Hz – 22. octave
> 97.090 Hz – 23. octave
> 194.181 Hz – 24. octave
> 388.361 Hz – 25. octave
> 776.723 Hz – 26. octave

A remark concerning the concert pitch:

At the Second International Standard Pitch Conference in London 1939, the frequency of the concert pitch »A'« was fixed at 440 Hz. The old concert pitch of 435 Hz is much closer to the chromatic »A'« of 435.92 Hz from the scale of the note corresponding to the day.
The original Parisian standard pitch tuning fork (Diapason normal) was made by Lissajous and had 435.4 Hz. This pitch was introduced by the French government in 1859 in cooperation with musicians such as Hector Berlioz, Meyerbeer and Rossini.

In 1950 the Académie des Sciences lowered the standard pitch for France to 432 Hz.

The Corresponding Color of the Day

The frequency of the 65th octave (rising) of a solar day lies within the visible range, for it is:

$$\frac{1}{86\,400\,sec} \cdot 2^{65} = 4.270 \cdot 10^{14}\ Hz$$

The frequency of $4.270 \cdot 10^{14}$ Hz corresponds to a wavelength of:

$$\lambda = \frac{c}{f} = \frac{2.997\,925 \cdot 10^{14}\ micrometer/sec}{4.270 \cdot 10^{14} \cdot 1/sec}$$
$$= 0.702\ micrometer$$

whereby »c« is the speed of light. Light with the frequency of $4.270 \cdot 10^{14}$ Hz, having a wavelength of 0.702 micrometer, we perceive as orange-red.
Orange-red is also the color traditionally worn by the »Sanyasins« (Indian mendicant monks).

It is noteworthy in this context that the carrier of the hereditary substance, DNA (Desoxyribonucleinacid) of which chromosomes consist, has a maximum of resonance at 0.351 micrometer (according to Popp, University of Marburg). 0.351 micrometer is precisely half the wavelength of the color of the day, 0.702 micrometer. The hereditary substance of man has a maximum of resonance which coincides with the 66th octave of the average solar day – the color of the Sanyasins is orange-red, and the 65th octave of the day generates as its first overtone this maximum of resonance!

THE SIDEREAL DAY

The daily rotation of the firmament is termed a sidereal day. At the end of a sidereal day the same stars reach their highest point, the upper culmination above the horizon. Astronomically the rhythm of the sidereal day is the basis of exact time measurement and calculation. Due to the annual motions of the sun from west to east, compared to the fixed stars, the sidereal day is about four minutes shorter than the average solar day. In other words, compared to the fixed stars the sun seems to fall behind by about 1° (degree) daily in easterly direction in the sphere.
The sidereal day has a duration of 23 hours 56 minutes 4.091 seconds, that is 86 164.091 seconds, corresponding to the frequency of:

$$\frac{1}{86\,164.091\,sec} = 1.160\,576 \cdot 10^{-5}\ Hz$$

Thus the 24th octave has a frequency of:
    $1.160\,576 \cdot 10^{-5}$ Hz $\cdot 2^{24} = 194.712...$ Hz
Thus the 25th has a frequency of:
    $2 \cdot 194.712$ Hz $= 389.425$ Hz
The difference in frequency compared to the average solar day in the 24th octave amounts to approximately half a Hertz (about 0.5 Hz), in the 25th octave about 1 Hz.
The corresponding chromatic »A'« of the note of the sidereal day at 194.712 Hz is 194.712 Hz $^{12}\sqrt{2^{14}} = 437.114$ Hz.
Transposed by octaves into the visible range, the 65 octave amounts to a frequency of $4.282 \cdot 10^{14}$ Hz, corresponding to a wavelength of 0.700 micrometer which in terms of color can hardly be differentiated from the transposed frequency of the average solar day.

e meter of a sidereal day is only slightly faster than
t of an average solar day. 23 hours, 56 minutes,
91 seconds are 1436.068 minutes, of which the
1 octave is a period of 0.021 913 minutes cor-
onding to a frequency of:

$$\frac{2^{16}}{1436.068 \ min} = 45.64 \ oscillations/min$$

e meter of 45.64 beats per minute corresponds to
16th octave of a sidereal day, twice that, 91.27
ts per minute, corresponds to the 17th octave of a
real day.

E YEAR

e earth's rotation around the sun. The orbital
ne of the earth's yearly rotation around the sun
nds tilted at a 23° 26' 32" degree angle (1978)
ards the earth's equator. The projection of this
ne on to the firmament is also known as the eclip-
'Greek: eklipsis = eclipse). The ecliptic intersects
celestial equator (the projection of the equatorial
ne onto the firmament) in two places, the vernal
inox (0° ♈; aries) and the autumnal equinox
≏; libra). The sun appears there in the northern
nisphere at the beginning of spring around the
nty-first of March (vernal equinox) and at the
inning of autumn around the twenty-third of Sep-
ber (autumnal equinox). At both equinoxes the
rises precisely in the east and sets precisely in the
t.

e period of time from one sun's passage of the
ng equinox till the next is called the tropical year.
ropical year has a duration of
i.242 198 79 days = 31 556 925.9747 seconds.

e Meter of a Tropical Year

ropical year has a duration of:
    31 556 925.9747 sec : 60 =
    525 948.7662 minutes.
e 24th octave thereof has a duration of:

$$\frac{525 \ 948.7662 \ min}{2^{24}} = 0.031 \ 349 \ minutes$$

which corresponds to a frequnecy of:

$$\frac{2^{24}}{525 \ 948.7662 min} = 31.899 \ vibrations \ per \ min$$

A meter of 31.899 beats per minute corresponds to
the twenty-fourth octave of a year, a meter of 63.798
beats per minute corresponds to the 25th octave of a
year, a meter of 127.596 beats per minute corresponds
to the 26th octave of a year.

The Corresponding Pendulum to a Tropical Year

According to the formula $l = \frac{T^2 \cdot g}{4\pi^2}$ (for explanation
see average solar day)
$T = 0.031 \ 349 \ min = 1.880 \ 94 \ sec$ (24th octave of
a tropical year)

$$l = \frac{1.880 \ 94 \ ^2 \ sec^2 \cdot 9.81 \ m \cdot sec^{-2}}{4\pi^2} = 0.879 \ meter$$

A pendulum with the length of about 88 cm oscillates in 1.88 sec, corresponding to the 24th octave of a
tropical year.

The Note of the Year

By forming the 32nd octave of the frequency of a
tropical year

$$\frac{1}{31 \ 556 \ 925.97 \ sec} \cdot 2^{32} = 136.102 \ 21 \ Hz$$

one arrives at a note which lies slightly below the
note »C#« (C# = C-sharp) in the chromatic scale.
Starting the calculation from an »A'« of 435.000 Hz,
the welltempered »C-sharp« has a frequency of:
    $435 \ Hz \cdot \sqrt[12]{2}^{-20} = 435 \ Hz \cdot 2^{-1.6}$
    $= 137.016 \ Hz$
To the tone of earth's year corresponds an »A'« of:
    $136.102 \ 21 \ Hz \cdot \sqrt[12]{2}^{20} = 136.102 \ 21 \ Hz$
    $\cdot 3.174 \ 80 \ Hz = 432.098 \ Hz$
In 1950 the Parisian Académie des Sciences lowered
the standard pitch for France to 432 Hz.
Ravi Shankar writes that the sitar (an Indian musical
instrument) should be tuned somewhat below the
European »C-sharp«. The basic note of the sitar, »Sa«
(Sadja, Indian basic note) thus corresponds to the
note of the year in the 32nd octave. For tuning purposes it is recommended to use a higher octave, for
example 272.20 Hz, since frequencies in the higher
octaves can be located by the human ear with greater
excactness.
Also the length of a sitar string is remarkable: with
most of the instruments measured, it was 88 cm. As
mentioned before, a pendulum of this length oscillates

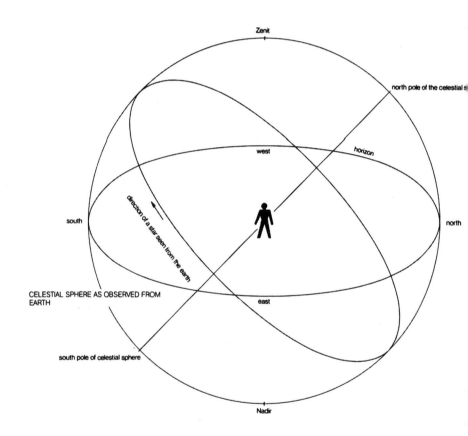

CELESTIAL SPHERE AS OBSERVED FROM
EARTH

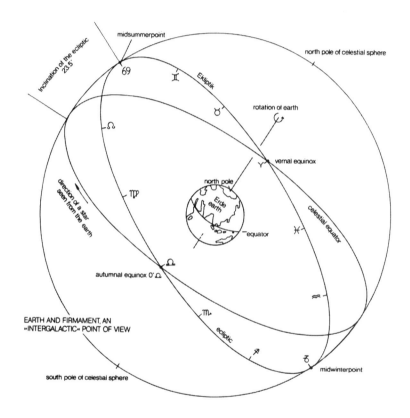

EARTH AND FIRMAMENT, AN
»INTERGALACTIC« POINT OF VIEW

in accordance to the octave of a year. »Sa«, the basic note of the sitar, is thus the $2^{(32-24)} = 2^8 = 256th$ overtone of a frequency of a pendulum with the length of a sitar string. So the sitar is exactly attuned to the year.

In Europe and North America there is a popular instrument with a string length of 88 cm, the electric bass guitar, without which rock music would be unthinkable. An examination of the bass guitar also reveals an interesting cosmic connection.

Light travels a distance of 88 cm in :

$$\frac{88 \ cm}{2.997\ 925 \cdot 10^{10}\ cm\ sec^{-1}} = 2.935\ 36 \cdot 10^{-9} sec$$

The corresponding frequency to this period of time is $3.406\ 73 \cdot 10^8$ Hz. Twenty octaves lower one obtaines a frequency of:
    $3.406\ 73 \cdot 10^8$ Hz : $2^{20} = 324.89$ Hz
which corresponds to an »E«. The bass guitar is normally tuned to an »E«. Remarkably enough this is also the 50th octave of an »apsiden« orbit rotation of the earth. Taking the sun as a central point of observation (heliocentric observation) the earth has an elliptical orbit around the sun, whereby the sun lies in a focal point of this ellipse. At times the earth is nearer to the sun (perihel), at times further away (aphel). Perihel and aphel are at the ends of the great axis of the earth's ellipse. This connecting axis is called the apsiden line, which completes a full rotation once every 110 000 years. The 50th octave of this period of rotation has a frequency of:

$$\frac{1}{110\ 000 \cdot 31\ 556\ 925\ sec} \cdot 2^{50} = 324.35\ Hz$$

The note of the resonance of the body of a violin is also said to be »C-sharp« (C#). Most data lie between 270 and 274 Hz. The 33rd octave of the frequency of the earth's year is 272.20 Hz. Thus the violin resounds in this range (±2 Hz).

The Colour of the Year

The 74th octave (rising) of a tropical year lies within the visible range; it is:
$$\frac{1}{31\ 556\ 925.97\ sec} \cdot 2^{74} = 5.986 \cdot 10^{14}\ Hz$$
This corresponds to a wavelength of 0.501 micrometer. This frequency and wavelength we perceive as blue – green.
Illustration: A sidereal year, the space of time between the sun's two passages of a certain star, lasts 365.256 360 42 days. That's about 20 minutes mor than a tropical year (due to the retrograde motion of the point of vernal equinox). This leads to a note with a frequency of 136.0969 Hz in the 32nd octave which is only $5.3 \cdot 10^{-3}$ Hz less than the note of the tropical year in the thirty-second octave. This difference is so minute as to be inaudible to the human ear.

THE PLATONIC YEAR

The earth revolves around its axis (from one pole to the other) and exhibits a cyroscopic motion. The shifting of the axis of a gyrating (gyrotation) or rotating body caused by external influences is called a precession, this is also the cause with the earth's axis due the attraction of sun and moon. This was already known in ancient times and the duration of the precession was said to be 25 920 years and was called the platonic year.
So the equinoctial points, reference points of astronomical coordinate systems, move along the ecliptic in westerly direction, at the rate of about 50 arc secon per year. Of all brighter stars it is Regulus, also known as Alpha Leonis, that stands closest to the ecliptic. Regulus (Latin: little king) is the brightest st in the constellation Leo, and in the ancient orient was known as the Regal Star.
Regulus now stands at a celestial longitude of abou 149° 33' (degrees). About 10 800 years ago the vernal equinox was close to the star Regulus. The mai star of the constellation Leo forms the peak of a triangle of nearly equal sides, the basis of which is line between Arctur and Spica.

The Meter of a Platonic Year

The 25 920 years of the platonic years correspond 1.363 $\cdot 10^{10}$ min. The 39th octave of this period ha duration of 0.024 80 minutes, which corresponds to a frequency of 40.33 beats per min.; the 40th octave to 80.65 beats per min., and the 41st octave to 161.31 beats per min.

The Pendulum of a Platonic Year

The 39th octave of a platonic year lasts 0.02480 min = 1.488 sec. According to the familiar formula:

$$l = \frac{T^2 \cdot g}{4\pi^2} \text{ one obtains:}$$

$$\frac{1.488^2 \, sec^2 \cdot 9.81 \, m \cdot sec^{-2}}{4\pi^2} = 0.550 \, meter$$

a pendulum of the length of 55 cm oscillates in a natural octave frequency of the platonic year.

The Note of the Platonic Year

Calculating the 47th octave of the frequency of the platonic year one obtains:

$$\frac{1}{31\ 556\ 925.97 \, sec} \cdot \frac{1}{25\ 920} \cdot 2^{47}$$
$$= 172.060 \, Hz$$

The next chromatic note is an »F« with a frequency of:
$$435 \, Hz \cdot \sqrt[12]{2}^{-16} = 435 \, Hz \cdot 2^{-1.3} =$$
$$435 \, Hz \cdot 0.39685 = 172.6299 \, Hz$$

The difference in frequencies is less than half a Hertz or 0.3% of the frequency of 172.060 Hz. The note »F« is indicated by the bass clef, (in the 47th octave, with a frequency of 172.06 Hz).

F   fa

The corresponding chromatic »A'« has a frequency of:

$$172.060 \, Hz \cdot \sqrt[12]{2}^{16} = 433.564 \, Hz$$

For vocal exercices and for the tuning of instruments it is recommended to use a tuning fork of a higher octave.

172,06 Hz – 47th octave
344.12 Hz – 48th octave
688.24 Hz – 49th octave

The Colors of the Platonic Year

The frequency of a platonic year (of 25920 years) transposed by octaves into the range of vision, is to be seen twice, at the lower and upper bounds of the visible range of human perception.
The 88th octave leads to a frequency of:

$$\frac{1}{31\ 556\ 925.97 \, sec \cdot 25\ 920} \cdot 2^{88} = 3.78 \cdot 10^{14} \, Hz$$

which corresponds to a wavelength of 0.792 micrometer which is seen as red at the lower end of the spectrum bordering on infra-red.
The 89th octave has a frequency of:
$$3.78 \cdot 10^{14} \, Hz \cdot 2 = 7.56 \cdot 10^{14} \, Hz$$
corresponding to a wavelength of 0.396 micrometer. This color we perceive as violet bordering on ultraviolet.

The platonic year transposed by octaves thus delimits roughly the visible range of human perception. If one forms a circle of colors by connecting the upper and lower bounds, as Goethe did in his »Theory of Colours«, then the »mystical union« coincides with the transposed frequencies of the platonic year.

HARMONICAL CONNECTIONS BETWEEN DAY, YEAR AND PLATONIC YEAR

Again and again it is apparent that the flow of the cosmos is orientated to simplest algebraic or geometrical structures.

The Corresponding Pendulum Lengths

The Day   : 43.2 cm
The Year   : 88 cm
The Platonic Year : 55 cm

A pendulum corresponding to the day is about half (or twice) as long as that of a year, since a pendulum octave (twice or half of the period of oscillation) equals four times the length of the pendulum.
The pendulum of the day: 10.8 cm   43.2 cm
                                        172.8 cm
The pendulum of the year: 5.5 cm   22 cm   88 cm
                                        352 cm
The ratios of length between a pendulum corresponding to a day and a pendulum of the platonic year are: 4:5, 1:5, 16:5, (4^n:5); from a year to a platonic year 2:5, or also 8:5, or 32:5 $\left(\dfrac{4^n}{2}:5\right)$, »n« equals any natural number, and can also be O.

THE CORRESPONDING EARTH NOTES

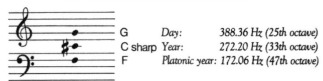

G	*Day:*	388.36 Hz (25th octave)
C sharp	*Year:*	272.20 Hz (33th octave)
F	*Platonic year:*	172.06 Hz (47th octave)

F F♯ G G♯ A A♯ *B* C C♯ D D♯ E F F♯ G

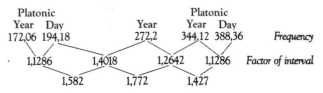

The note of the day has a ratio to the year's note of:
    1 : 1.4018
The year's note has a ratio to the day's note of:
    1 : 1.4267
In both cases this corresponds to a tritone (tritone =
3 whole notes = 6 half notes)
A diatonic tritone of:
    $1 : \frac{45}{32} = 1 : 1.406\ 25$
A chromatic tritone of:
    $1 : \sqrt[12]{2^6} = 1 : \sqrt{2} = 1 : 1.414\ 213\ 562$
A diatonic tritone of:
    $1 : \frac{64}{45} = 1 : 1.4\overline{2}$

In terms of algebra that means:
$$\frac{1}{Day} \cdot 2^n : \frac{1}{Year} \cdot 2^{(8+n)} \approx$$
$$\frac{1}{Year} \cdot 2^{(9+n)} : \frac{1}{Day} \cdot 2^n$$

wherby n = 0 or n = any whole number.

The two diatonic tritones with the frequency ratios of
$1 : \frac{45}{32}$ and $1 : \frac{64}{45}$ differ by the small intervall of:

$1 : \frac{2048}{2025} = 1 : 1.011\ 358...$ the so called Diachisma.

The chromatic tritone lies in-between: $1 : \sqrt{2} =$
1 : 1.414... and forms the axis of symmetry around
which the classical intervals group themselves in
pairs. For example a fourth $(1 : \frac{4}{3})$ and a fifth

: $\frac{3}{2}$) *share the same interval to a chromatic* *tone:*

$\sqrt{2} : \frac{4}{3} = 1.41421 : 1.\bar{3} = 1.060\ 660$
$\frac{3}{2} : \sqrt{2} = 1.5 : 1.41421 = 1.060\ 660$

le frequency of the day and the frequency of the *atonic year, both transposed by octaves, stand in a* *tio of:* $1 : 1.772$, *that corresponds to the chromatic* *nor seventh of:* $1 : \sqrt[12]{2^{10}} = 1 : 1.782$ *or the diato-* *: minor seventh of:* $1 : \frac{16}{9} = 1 : 1.\bar{7}$.

n the other hand the transposed frequency of the *atonic year stands to the tone of the day in a ratio* $1 : 1.1286$, *that corresponds to the chromatic* *jor second of:* $1 : \sqrt[12]{2^2} = 1.12246...$ *or the* *atonic whole note of:* $1 : \frac{9}{8} = 1 : 1.125$

le transposed frequency of the year stands in a ratio $1 : 1.2642$ *to the transposed frequency of the pla-* *ic year, which corresponds to the chromatic major* *rd of:* $1 : \sqrt[12]{2^4} = 1 : 1.2599...$ *or more or less to* *diatonic major third of:* $1 : \frac{5}{4} = 1 : 1.25$ *or more* *cisely to the diminished minor fourth of:* $1 : \frac{512}{405} = 1.264\ 197\ 5...$

le transposed frequency of the platonic year stands *a ratio of:* $1 : 1.582$ *to the transposed frequency* *the year.*

at corresponds to the chromatic minor sixth of: $\sqrt[12]{2^8} = 1 : 1.587$ *or approximately to a diatonic* *th of:* $1 : \frac{8}{5} = 1 : 1.6$ *or more exactly to an aug-* *nted fifth of:* $1 : \frac{405}{256} = 1 : 1.5820$

E EGYPTIAN UNITS OF LENGTH AND E EARTH NOTES

cording to the sources of John Michell as explained *his book »City of Revelation«, the ancient Egyp-* *as used mainly three units of measurement in their* *hitecture:*

the Remen: $= 1.2165$ feet ≈ 37.1 cm
the Royal Cubit: $= 1.72$ feet ≈ 52.4 cm
the Megalithic Yard: $= 2.72$ feet ≈ 82.9 cm

e ratio of Remen : Royal cubit : Meg. yard
$: \sqrt{2} : \sqrt{5}$

1 Remen²	$= 1.48$	feet²
	$= (0.74 \cdot 2)$	feet²
1 Royal Cubit²	$= 2.96$	feet²
	$= (074 \cdot 4)$	feet²
1 Megalith Yard²	$= 7.4$	feet²
	$= (0.74 \cdot 10)$	feet²

THE EARTH'S MOON

The period of the moon can be defined in different ways (always in average solar time). The synodic month is the time between two moon phases of the same kind (e.g., from full moon to full moon or from new moon to new moon) and has a duration of 29 days, 12 hours, 44 minutes and 2.8 seconds. The synodic month, which is also called »lunation«, can be easily perceived even with untrained eyes. The sidereal month is the time between the moon's two successive passings of the same star (more precisely: through the same circle of hours of the star). It has a duration of 27 days, 7 hours, 43 minutes and 11.5 seconds.

Besides, there is also:

a tropic month (the space of time between the moon's two successive passings through the circle of hours of the spring equinox: 27 days, 7 h 43 min. 4.7 sec.), an anomalistic month (the time between two succes- sive passings of the moon through the perigee, the point where the moon is closest to the earth: 27 days, 13 h 18 min. 33.2 sec.), a draconitic month (the space of time between two successive passings of the moon through the rising moon node: 27 days, 5 h 5 min. 35.8 sec.).

These three »months« differ only slightly from the sidereal month, but they are of great relevance for the calculation of lunar and solar eclipses. The especially long duration of the synodic month as compared with the sidereal month is a consequence of the movement of the earth around the sun, or of the sun's apparent movement through the ecliptic. After one sidereal month the sun has moved on about 28° on the ecliptic, and the moon needs about $2\frac{1}{4}$ days more to »catch up with« the sun and so to reach the next new moon phase. See the picture next page.

(Synod = gathering or meeting, here of sun and moon at new moon, when sun and moon are in conjunc- tion with each other – at full moon they are in oppo- sition. Sidereal revolution = revolution in relation to the fixed stars.)

If one calculates the exact length according to these
specifications, the result is:

1 Remen	$-\sqrt{1.48\ feet^2}$	$-1.216\ 533\ feet$
	$-0.370805\ m$	
1 Royal Cubit	$-\sqrt{2.96\ feet^2}$	$-1.720\ 465\ feet$
	$-0.524\ 398\ m$	
1 Megalith Yard	$-\sqrt{7.4\ feet^2}$	$-2.720\ 294\ feet$
	$-0.829\ 146\ m$	

In subatomic physics as in astronomy the time light
takes to cover a certain distance is used as a measuring unit of these distances. (One light year equals
$9.460\ 5 \cdot 10^{12}$ km $-63\ 240$ astronomical units)
Light travels at a speed of:
$(2.997\ 925 \pm 0.000\ 001) \cdot 10^{10}$ cm/sec
$(299\ 793$ km/sec)
By calculating the time light takes to cover a Remen,
a Royal Cubit or a Megalithic Yard and then the
corresponding frequency which is transposed by octaves, one finds an astonishing accordance between
Egyptian units of measure with the notes derived
from the earth's orbit.

Remen	Royal Cubit	Megalithic Yard	
37,0 805	52,4 398	82,9 146	Length in cm:
			Frequency:
$\dfrac{2{,}997925 \cdot 10^{10}\ \text{cm/sec}}{37{,}0805\ \text{cm}}$	$\dfrac{2{,}997925 \cdot 10^{10}\ \text{cm/sec}}{52{,}4398\ \text{cm}}$	$\dfrac{2{,}997925 \cdot 10^{10}\ \text{cm/sec}}{82{,}9146\ \text{cm}}$	$\left(\begin{array}{c}\text{speed of light}\\ \text{distance}\end{array}\right)$
▬	▬	▬	
$8{,}084910 \cdot 10^8$ Hz	$5{,}716889 \cdot 10^8$ Hz	$3{,}615678 \cdot 10^8$ Hz	
-22	-22	-22	Number of octave
$\dfrac{8{,}084910 \cdot 10^8\ \text{Hz}}{2^{22}}$	$\dfrac{5{,}716889 \cdot 10^8\ \text{Hz}}{2^{22}}$	$\dfrac{3{,}615678 \cdot 10^8\ \text{Hz}}{2^{22}}$	Frequency:
▬	▬	▬	
192,76 Hz	136,30 Hz	86,20 Hz	
Tageston	Jahreston	Ton des plat. Jahres	in comparison:
Note of the Day	Note of the Year	Note of the Platonic Year	
194,18 Hz	136,10 Hz	86,03 Hz	
1,42 Hz	0,2 Hz	0,17 Hz	Difference:

A Remen corresponds to the note of the day, »G«,
a Royal Cubit to the note of the year, »C-sharp«
and a Megalithic Yard to the note of the
platonic year, »F«.

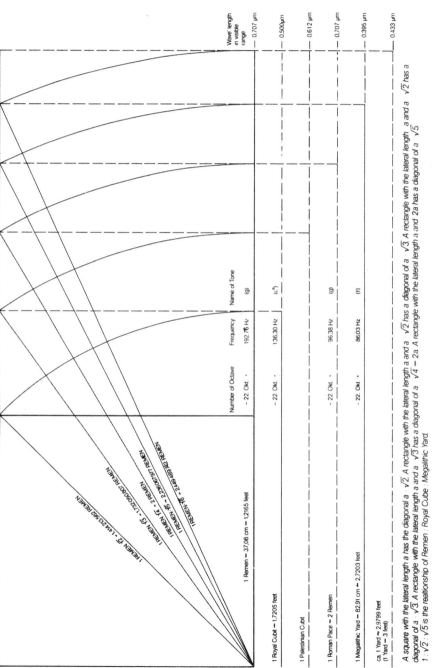

A square with the lateral length a has the diagonal a · √2. A rectangle with the lateral length a and a · √2 has a diagonal of a · √3. A rectangle with the lateral length a and a · √3 has a diagonal of a · √4 = 2a. A rectangle with the lateral length a and 2a has a √2 has a diagonal of a · √3. A rectangle with the lateral length a and 2a has a diagonal of a · √5.
1 : √2 : √5 is the realtionship of Remen : Royal Cube : Megalithic Yard

THE EARTH. THE EARTH'S MOON. THE SUN.

A short consideration of the proportions of sun, earth and moon.

The old system of measurement in miles is far more interrelated to the proportions of our solar system than the metric system. It is easier to express distances in miles in short algebraic formulas.

The earth's diameter:	7 920 miles $= \frac{11!}{7!}$ miles $= 8 \cdot 9 \cdot 10 \cdot 11$ miles	
The earth's radius:	3 960 miles $\quad = 6 \cdot 660$ miles	

The moon's diameter:	2 160 miles $\quad = 6 \cdot 6 \cdot 60$ miles	
The moon's radius:	1 080 miles $\quad = 10 \cdot 108$ miles	

The earth's radius:	3 960 miles
The moon's radius:	1 080 miles
Rad. earth + rad. moon:	5 040 miles $= 7!$ miles $= 1 \cdot 2 \cdot 3 \cdot 4 \cdot 5 \cdot 6 \cdot 7$ miles

Distance earth-moon: 237 600 miles $= 60$ earth radius $= 6 \cdot 60 \cdot 660$
The diameter
of the sun is: 864 000 miles $= 10 \cdot 86\ 400$ miles $= 12 \cdot 12 \cdot 600$ miles
$\qquad\qquad\qquad$ 86 400 sec $\quad\rightarrow$ *duration of an average solar day*
$\qquad\qquad$ 864 000 : 2 $= 432\ 000 \rightarrow$ *The sun's radius is: 432 000 miles*
There are $\qquad\qquad\qquad\qquad\qquad \rightarrow$ *A Kali Yuga lasts: 432 000 miles*

$1 \cdot 108 =$	108	$\rightarrow$ *number of pearls on a buddhist mala*
$10 \cdot 108 =$	1 080	$\rightarrow$ *number of miles $\rightarrow$ the moon's radius*
$100 \cdot 108 =$	10 800	$\rightarrow$ *number of stanzas in the Rigveda*

of 40 syllables each
$\qquad\qquad$ 40 $\cdot$ 10 800 $= 432\ 000 \rightarrow$ *432 000 syllables in the Rigveda*
$\qquad\qquad\qquad\qquad\qquad\qquad$ 432 000 miles $=$ *sun's radius*
$\qquad\qquad\qquad\qquad\qquad\qquad$ 432 000 years $=$ *Kali Yuga*

	$= 10\ 800$	$\rightarrow$ *About 10 800 years ago the vernal equinox was near the star Regulus (Alpha Leonis).*
$1000 \cdot 108 = 108\ 000$		$\rightarrow \frac{1}{4}$ *of a Kali Yuga $=$ 1 Kali Yuga season*
	$= 108\ 000$	$\rightarrow 30 \cdot 60 \cdot 60 =$ *the number of seconds per zodiacal sign*

The moon and the number 108

$1 \cdot 108 =$	108	$\rightarrow$ *is the atomic weight of silver, the element traditionally associated with the moon*
$20 \cdot 108 =$	2 160	$\rightarrow$ *number of miles of the moon's diameter*
	2 160	$\rightarrow$ *number of years a platonic month is lasting*
$240 \cdot 108 =$	25 920	$\rightarrow$ *number of years a platonic year is lasting*
$\frac{1}{4} \cdot 108 =$	27	$\rightarrow$ *number of days of the duration of a sidereal revolution of the moon (27,321 661 days $=$ 27 days, 7 hours, 43 minutes, 11.5 seconds)*
$\frac{1}{6} \cdot 108 =$	18	$\rightarrow$ *number of years of the duration of a saros-period (cycle of eclipsis). (exactly: 18 years, 11 days, 7 hours, 42 minutes.)*

Kali Yuga $\qquad\qquad\qquad\qquad \rightarrow$ *Sanskrit Kal $=$ to measure (calculate) Kala, $=$ mother of the spirit of the ag*

The moon's synodic and sidereal period of revolution have a ratio of: 100 : 108 (exactly : 100 : 108.084 8)

In Comparison: Our Modern Units of Measurement
(1 English mile = 1.609 344 km)

	Old units of measurement	I.R.E. (Hayford 1909) I.R.E. (Hayford 1909)	W.G.S Geodätisches Weltsystem 1961 G.W.S. (Geodesic world system)
rad. of equator = a		6 378,383 km 3 963,347 Meilen/miles	6 378,163 km 3 963,207 Meilen/miles
rad. of pole axis = b		6 356,912 km 3 950,002 Meilen/miles	6 356,777 km 3 949,918 Meilen/miles
$\frac{\sqrt{a \cdot b} + a}{2}$ Average radius exactitude	3 960 Meilen/miles 6 373,002 km	3 960,008 Meilen/miles 1,92 mm/km	3 959,882 Meilen/miles 29,85 mm/km

	Old Units of Measurement	Modern Data dtv »Atlas of Astronomy«
The moon's diameter	3 476.18 km 2 160 miles	3 476.00 km 2 159.89 miles
The sun's diameter	1 390 473.1 km 864 000 miles	1 392 000 km 864 949 miles
The average distance between earth and moon	382 380 km 237 600 miles	384 400 km 238 855 miles

The Total of the Digits of the Mile Units:

The earth's diameter → 7920 miles →
7 + 9 + 2 + 0 = 18;   1 + 8 = 9

The moon's diameter → 2 160 miles →
2 + 1 + 6 + 0   = 9;

The sun's diameter → 864 000 miles →
8 + 6 + 4 + 0 = 18;   = 1 + 8 = 9

The earth's + the moon's diam. → 5 040 miles →
5 + 4 + 0   = 9

The distance earth/moon → 237 600 miles →
2 + 3 + 7 + 6 = 18;   1 + 8 = 9

The beads of the mala → 108 → 1 + 0 + 8 = 9
The sid. period of the moon = 27 days → 2 + 7 = 9

The duration of pregnancy → 9 months (synodic)

NEW MOON POSITION
ON 2. OKTOBER 1978

*On 2. October 1978 at 6 h 41' world time there
was a Sun-Moon conjunction, that is, new
moon, in the sign of Libra at 8° 44'. Mercury was
almost in conjunction with Sun and Moon. At 20
h 47' world time of the same day a Moon-Pluto
conjunction took place.*
*After one sideral month the Moon again passed
the 8° 44' mark in Libra. This took place in the
early afternoon of 29. October 1978. At that time
however, the sun was already in the sign of
Scorpio, so that the Moon had to move on
through the ecliptic for another 2¼ days before
catching up with the sun again.*

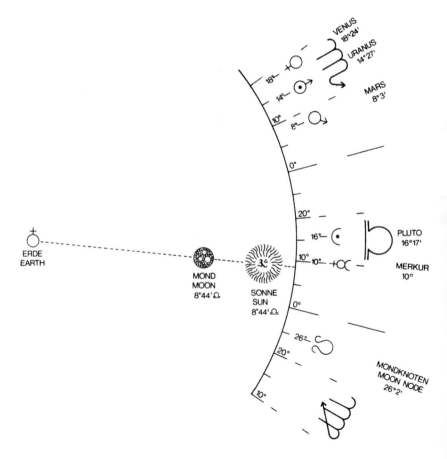

NEW MOON POSITION ON 31. OCTOBER 1978

On 31. October 1978 at 20 h 07', sun and moon were again in conjunction, at 8° 3' Scorpio. The Moon had travelled through 13 signs of the zodiac to be once more in conjunction with the Sun. In one sideral month, the Moon travels through 12 signs of the zodiac, in one synodic month through 13. The synodic month, the length of time from one new moon to the next, comprises about 29½ days, one month.

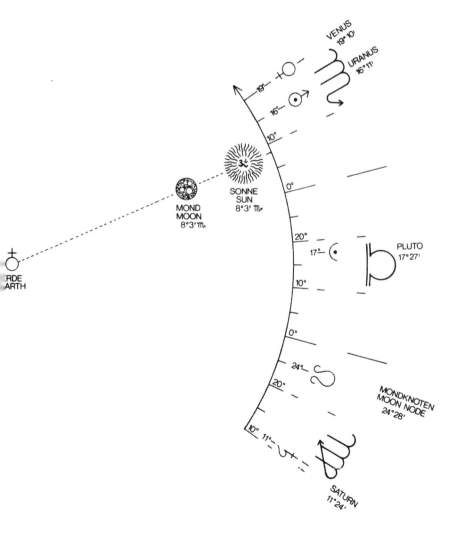

On October 2, 1978 at 6 h 41 min *world time* (Greenwich time — Western European time) *new moon* (sun-moon conjunction) *was at* $8°44'$ *Libra* (♎). On October 29, 1978 the moon again passed the $8°44'$ mark in Libra. The next conjunction of moon and sun (i.e. the next new moon) however did not take place until October 31, 1978 at 20 h 07 min world time at $8°03'$ Scorpio (♏).

THE FREQUENCIES OF THE MOON

The Synodic Month

The synodic month has a duration of 29 days, 12 h., 44 min, 2.8 sec, that is 42 524.047 minutes or 2 551 442.8 seconds.

The Meter of the Synodic Month

The synodic period has a duration of 42 524.047 minutes. The period of the 21st octave has a duration of:

$$\frac{42\ 524.047\ min}{2^{21}} = 0.020\ 277\ min.$$

This corresponds to a frequency of:

$$\frac{1}{0.020\ 277\ min} = 49.32\ vibrations/min.$$

The meter of 49.32 beats/min corresponds to the 21st octave of the synodic month. The meter of 98.63 beats/min corresponds to the 22nd octave of the synodic month. The meter of 197.27 beats/min corresponds to the 23rd octave of the synodic month.

The Tone of the Synodic Month

The synodic period has a duration of 2 551 442.8 seconds, corresponding to the frequency of:

$$\frac{1}{2\ 551\ 442.8\ sec} = 3.919\ 351 \cdot 10^{-7}\ Hz$$

The 29th octave therefore has the frequency of: $3.919\ 351 \cdot 10^{-7}\ Hz \cdot 2^{29} = 210.419\ Hz$ and the 30th octave has the frequency of: $210.419\ Hz \cdot 2 = 420.837\ Hz$. This tone is nowadays called »G$^{#}$« (G sharp); in the 18th century it was still an »A«.

In Europe, during the last centuries the concert pitch changed constantly and varied also from country to country. In India and Tibet however, the basic note has a long tradition and — in contrast to Europe — has always been in harmony with the rotation of the earth in the solar system — therefore it still has its validity! There, bells and instruments are frequently attuned to the tone of the earth's year (SA — Sadja).

At the height of European musical art — baroque and classic — the concert pitch was about one half note lower than today and in harmony with the tone of the synodic month. Mozart's tuning-fork, for example, had 421.6 Hz, Händel's (of 1751) 422.5 Hz. Händel was certainly one of the first composers whom a tuning-fork was available, since it was invented by a trumpet player of his orchestra, John Shore, in 1711. In 1810, the concert pitch of the Paris Opera was 423 Hz, about 2 Hz higher than the tone of the 30th octave of the synodic month.

It should be mentioned that the note of 423 Hz, though very close to the tone of the 30th octave of the synodic month, 420.837 Hz, is even closer to the tone of the 41st octave of Neptune (not yet discovered then) which has a frequency of 422.90 Hz. Synodic month and Neptune are almost in harmony! To make a symphony in C major by Mozart sound like it did at the time of its composition, it would have to be played in B major today, to compensate for the rising of the concert pitch.

The multiplication of a »G$^{#}$« of 420.837 Hz with $^{12}\sqrt{2} = 1.\ 059\ 463$ leads to an »A« of $420.837 \cdot 1.059\ 463 = 445.861\ Hz$. Electronic tuning machine with chromatic scale and a scale indicator for the note »A« have to be adjusted to 445.861 Hz. If the the »G$^{#}$« is generated, you hear the frequency of 420.837 Hz or, depending on the adjustment, the double frequency of 841.674 Hz or the half frequency of 210.419 Hz.

The Color of the Synodic Month

Light with a frequency equal to the 70th octave of the frequency of the synodic moon period is visible and has the frequency of $3.919\ 351 \cdot 10^{-7}\ Hz \cdot 2^{70} = 4.627 \cdot 10^{14}\ Hz$ This corresponds to a wave-lenght of 0.648 micrometer. This frequency and wave-lenght we perceive as orange.

THE SIDEREAL MONTH

The sidereal month has a duration of 27 days, 7 h 43 min, 11.5 sec, that is 39 343.192 minutes or 2.360 591 5 $\cdot 10^6$ seconds.

The Meter of the Sidereal Month

The 21st octave of the period of 39 343.192 min has duration of

$$\frac{39\,343.192\ min.}{2^{21}} = 0.018\,760\ min.$$

corresponding to a frequency of 53.30 vibrations/min. The meter of the sidereal month has:
- the 21st octave   53.30 beats/min,
- the 22nd octave 106.61 beats/min,
- the 23rd octave 213.22 beats/min.

The Tone of the Sidereal Month

The frequency of the sidereal moon period is:

$$\frac{1}{2.360\,5915 \cdot 10^6\,sec} = 4.236\,226\,4 \cdot 10^{-7}\ Hz.$$

The 29th octave therefore has the frequency of:
$$4.236\,226\,4 \cdot 10^{-7} \cdot 2^{29}\ Hz = 227.431\ Hz$$
The next chromatic note, taking an »A'« of 435 Hz, an »A*« (A sharp). Electronic tuning machines with chromatic scale and a scale indicator for the note »A'« have to be adjusted to 429.332 Hz. If then the »A*« is generated, you hear the frequency of 227.431 Hz, or 454.861 Hz respectively. It is also possible to get an »A'« of 454.861 Hz out of the electronic tuning machines from the start, if the »A'« has been adjusted to that frequency. The naming of the notes is always relative, that is, depending on the basic note or concert pitch. So, in relation to an »A'« = 435 Hz, the frequency of 454.861 Hz is an »A*«, in relation to an »A'« = 442.46 Hz however it is a slightly raised »A'«, since the limit between »A'« and A*« lies slightly above the frequency of the sidereal month. The scope of the notes in the chromatic tuning system with the half note interval of $^{12}\sqrt{2} = 1.05946$ $^{24}\sqrt{2} = 1.029\,302$. For an »A'« of 435 Hz, frequencies from 435 : $^{24}\sqrt{2} = 422.616$ Hz to 435 · $^{24}\sqrt{2} = 447.746$ Hz are correlated to the »A'«. For an »A'« of 422.46 Hz, frequencies from 442.46 : $^{24}\sqrt{2} = 429.86$ Hz to 442.46 · $^{24}\sqrt{2} = 455.43$ Hz are correlated to the »A'«.

The names of notes used in this book relate to an »A'« 435 Hz, the so-called Old Parisian Concert Pitch. Light with a frequency equal to the 70th octave of the frequency of the) sidereal month is visible and has a frequency of:
$$4.236\,226\,4 \cdot 10^{-7}\ Hz \cdot 2^{70} = 5.001 \cdot 10^{14}\ Hz$$
and a wave-lenght of 0.599 micrometer. This frequency we perceive as yellow-orange.

COLORS AND NOTES OF THE SIDEREAL PLANET ROTATIONS

Since Venus has always been considered the planet of the fine arts, in this book only Venus will be introduced in detail; the other planets have been summarized in tables. The method for calculating the notes and colors is the same for all the planets. A summary of this method will be given also in the table appendix: »Illustrations and Annotations to the Table of Periods and Frequencies«.
In Europe, the Venus tuning is being used more and more often; therefore frequency tables for diatonic as well as for chromatic tuning have been calculated and added. For the diatonic tuning, for every note the corresponding »A'« has been added, so that electronic tuning machines can also be used for diatonic tuning.

VENUS

In Paracelsus's opinion, too few look up to to the starry skies »from which an incessant stream of enlightenment is flowing which is leading mankind to new sciences and new arts. Music, for example, comes from the planet Venus. If all musicians would open themselves to the influence of her light, they would create a more beautiful, more heavenly music than the hitherto existing.«

The Meter of Venus

The sidereal period of Venus has a duration of 224.7008 days or 323 569.15 minutes or 19 414 149 seconds.
The period of the 24th octave has a duration of:
$$\frac{323\,569.15\ min}{2^{24}} = 0.019\,286\ min.$$
corresponding to the frequency of:
$$\frac{1}{0.019\,286\ min.} = 51.85\ beats/min.$$
The meter of Venus has:
in the 24th octave   51.85 beats/min.
in the 25th octave 103.70 beats/min.

The Tone of Venus

The frequency of the sidereal period of Venus, raised into the 32nd octave, vibrates at a frequency of:

$$\frac{1}{19\ 414\ 149} \cdot 2^{32} \text{ Hz} = 221.229 \text{ Hz};$$

raised into the 33rd octave, it vibrates at a frequency of:

$$\frac{1}{19\ 414\ 149} \cdot 2^{33} \text{ Hz} = 442.457 \text{ Hz}.$$

So the chromatic, welltempered Venus scale has the following frequencies (the interval factor being $\sqrt[12]{2} = 1.059\ 463\ 09...$):

A   221.229 Hz (32nd octave)
A$^{\#}$ 234.384 Hz
B   248.321 Hz   Higher octaves,
C   263.087 Hz   corresponding to the number
C$^{\#}$ 278.731 Hz   of the octave:
D   295.305 Hz   the 2-, 4-, 8-, 16-fold
D$^{\#}$ 312.865 Hz   of the given frequencies
E   331.469 Hz   for the 1st, 2nd, 3rd, 4th higher octave.
F   351.179 Hz   Lower octaves:
F$^{\#}$ 372.061 Hz   correspondingly $\frac{1}{2}$, $\frac{1}{4}$, $\frac{1}{8}$, $\frac{1}{16}$ of
G   394.185 Hz   the given frequencies.
G$^{\#}$ 417.624 Hz
A'   442.457 Hz (33rd octave)

The welltempered tuning was introduced in the European occident by Andreas Werkmeister, born November 30, 1645 in Beneckenstein. Before that it had not been possible to play all keys on the same keyboard without having to tune anew. In China, the chromatic scale had been calculated already 50 years before Werkmeister's birth: as early as 1595, Prince Chu Tsai Yü calculated the exponents of the $\sqrt[12]{2}$ –row up to nine places after the decimal point.

The tuning system of Andreas Werkmeister inspired Johann Sebastian Bach to his famous composition »Das wohltemperierte Klavier«.

In the chromatic tuning system, the interval factor from semitone to semitone is always constant ($\sqrt[12]{2} = 1.059\ 463...$). In the diatonic tuning system which is based on the natural overtone series and which has pure (beatless/synchronized) thirds, fourths and fifths, the interval factors of the intervals between semitones are not constant.

The lenght of the vibrating part of the string is in reverse proportionality to the frequency.
If, for example, $\frac{1}{1}$ of the string (tonic) sounds with the basic frequency n,

then $\frac{1}{2}$ of the string (octave)
will sound with the frequency of 2 n,
$\frac{1}{3}$ of the string (octave + fifth = twelfth)
will sound with the frequency of 3 n,
$\frac{2}{3}$ of the string (fifth)
will sound with the frequency of $\frac{3}{2}$ n.
$\frac{1}{4}$ of the string (double octave)
will sound with the frequency of 4 n,
$\frac{3}{4}$ of the string (fourth)
will sound with the frequency of $\frac{4}{3}$ n
$\frac{1}{5}$ of the string (double octave + major third)
will sound with the frequency of 5 n,
$\frac{2}{5}$ of the string (octave + major third)
will sound with the frequency of $\frac{5}{2}$ n
$\frac{3}{5}$ of the string (major sixth)
will sound with the frequency of $\frac{5}{3}$ n
$\frac{4}{5}$ of the string (major third)
will sound with the frequency of $\frac{5}{4}$ n
$\frac{1}{6}$ of the string (double octave + fifth)
will sound with the frequency of 6 n,
$\frac{5}{6}$ of the string (minor third)
will sound with the frequency of $\frac{6}{5}$ n

Johannes Kepler, who derives, establishes and explaines the complete setting into music of a horoscope (the illustration of the constellations of the planets at a certain time and a certain place) in his World Harmonic (»Harmonices Mundi«, Lincii, Austria, 1619) uses the following diatonic scale, upon which he comments in book III, chapter 8:
»So on the whole an octave receives 13 strings with the following smallest numbers or proportional links; between these numbers I have inserted all smallest intervals after their natural order in a complete and wholly organic system.«

in the usual notes	melodic or quasi-melodic intervals	length of string (free units of length)	

		1080	high
	semitone		
		1152	
	limma		
		1215	
	semitone		
		1296	
	diesis		
		1350	
	semitone		
		1440	
	semitone		
		1536	
	limma		
		1620	
	semitone		
		1728	
	diesis		
		1800	
	semitone		
		1920	
	semitone		
		2048	
	limma		
		2160	low

In his considerations, Kepler proceeds from a »G« which he correlates to the earth because of the relations of the velocities of the orbits (G, like Geo, Greek for 'earth'. »G« is the 5th note in the present system starting with »C«, and geo-metry in Greece was the so-called 5th science.)

Rudolf Steiner, the founder of anthroposophy, in his system proceeded from a »C« of 256 Hz. Steiner simply octavated the second: 1 sec correlates with 1 Hz; the octaves then have simply squares as their frequencies: 2 Hz, 4 Hz, 8 Hz, 16 Hz, 32 Hz, 64 Hz, 128 Hz, 256 Hz.

For comparison: the chromatic C calculated from
an »A'« — 435 Hz:
C — 258.65 Hz

the note of the day, »G« — 194.18 Hz:
C — 259.20 Hz

the note of the year, »C-sharp« — 136.10 Hz:
C — 256.93 Hz

the note of the platonic year, »F« — 86.03 Hz:
C — 257.80 Hz

the note of the Venus, »A'« — 442.46 Hz:
C — 263.09 Hz

The calculation of the frequencies of the diatonic
scale for the Venus-A — 442,457 Hz gives the following results:

name of interval	interval factor	interval factor of the semitone interval	name of note		frequency
basic note	1	–	a	A	221,229
minor second	$\frac{135}{128}$ — 1,054687	$\frac{135}{128}$	(a#)	(A#)	233,327
major second	$\frac{9}{8}$ — 1,125	$\frac{16}{15}$	h	B	248,882
minor third	$\frac{6}{5}$ — 1,2	$\frac{16}{15}$	c	C	265,474
major third	$\frac{5}{4}$ — 1,25	$\frac{25}{24}$	(c#)	(C#)	276,536
fourth	$\frac{4}{3}$ — 1,$\overline{3}$	$\frac{16}{15}$	d	D	294,972
tritone	$\frac{45}{32}$ — 1,40625	$\frac{135}{128}$	(d#)	(D#)	311,103
fifth	$\frac{3}{2}$ — 1,5	$\frac{16}{15}$	e	E	331,843
minor sixth	$\frac{8}{5}$ — 1,6	$\frac{16}{15}$	f	F	353,966
major sixth	$\frac{5}{3}$ — 1,$\overline{6}$	$\frac{25}{24}$	(f#)	(F#)	368,715
minor seventh	$\frac{16}{9}$ — 1,$\overline{7}$	$\frac{16}{15}$	g	G	393,295
major seventh	$\frac{15}{8}$ — 1,875	$\frac{135}{128}$	(g#)	(G#)	414,804
Oktave octave	2	$\frac{16}{15}$	a'	A'	442.457

*The notes A B C D E F G A correlate precisely with
the diatonic A minor scale; the major scale consists
of A B C♯ D E F♯ G♯ A, called A major.*

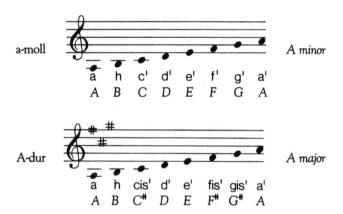

a-moll   A minor

a	h	c'	d'	e'	f'	g'	a'
A	B	C	D	E	F	G	A

A-dur   A major

a	h	cis'	d'	e'	fis'	gis'	a'
A	B	C♯	D	E	F♯	G♯	A

To measure or generate diatonic intervals with chromatic tuning machines, the corresponding »A'« has to
be calculated for every interval or for every frequency
if the machine indicates only the frequencies around
»A'«.

Venus scale (diatonic; corresponding chromatic A')

name of note	frequency in Hz (diat. scale)	frequency in Hz (corr. chromatic A')
A	221.229	→ 442.46
A♯	233.327	→ 440.46
B	248,882	→ 443.46
C	265.474	→ 446.47
C♯	276.536	→ 438.97
D	294.972	→ 441.96
D♯	311.103	→ 439.97
E	331.843	→ 442.96
F	353.966	→ 445.97
F♯	368.715	→ 438.48
G	393,295	→ 441.46
G♯	414.804	→ 439.47
A'	442.457	→ 442.46

THE MANDALA OF VENUS

*The sidereal period of Venus has a duration of
aboout 0.615 tropical years, that is more or less the
Golden Mean of the year of Earth. Therefore Sun-
Venus conjunctions (as seen from the planet Earth)
take place fairly precisely in pentagon points at the
ecliptic. This cycle is repeated every 8 years, in which
time the points have shifted about 1.5°. The Sun-
Venus conjunction which takes place after 8 years at
almost the same point is of the same kind, that is, it is
either an upper (Venus behind Sun) or a lower
(Venus between Sun and Earth) conjunction again.
After every 4 years a conjunction of the opposite type
takes place at the same point: after an upper one a
lower one, and vice versa. Within 8 years Venus thus
forms a five-leaved lotus at the sky.
That Venus can sometimes be seen as the morning
star and sometimes as the evening star depends on the
type of the preceding conjunction: after a lower conjunction, Venus can be seen as the morning star, after
an upper conjunction as the evening star.*

The Sun-Venus Conjunctions:

5 Con-junc-tions	upper conj. 1978 Jan. 22,	2°	Aquarius	
				diff. ca. 77°
	lower conj. 1978 Nov. .7,	15°	Scorpio	
				diff. ca. 73°
	upper conj. 1979 Aug. 25,	2°	Virgo	
				diff. ca. 68°
	lower conj. 1980 Jun. 15,	24°	Gemini	
				diff. ca. 67°
	upper conj. 1981 Apr. 7,	17°	Aries	
				diff. ca. 76°
5 Con-junc-tions	lower conj. 1982 Jan. 21,	1°	Aquarius	
				diff. ca. 80°
	upper conj. 1982 Nov. 4,	11°	Scorpio	
				diff. ca. 70°
	lower conj. 1983 Aug. 25,	1°	Virgo	
				diff. ca. 66°
	upper conj. 1984 Jun. 15,	25°	Gemini	
				diff. ca. 71°
	lower conj. 1985 Apr. 3,	14°	Aries	
				diff. ca. 75°
	upper conj. 1986 Jan. 19,	29°	Capricorn	
				diff. ca. 76°
	lower conj. 1986 Nov. 5,	13'	Scorpio	

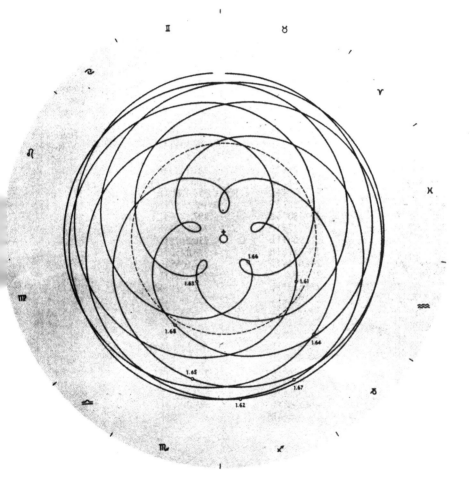

CROMATIC FREQUENCES

Trop. Jahres-Stimmung	Plat. Jahres-Stimmung	
tropical year tuning	*platonic year tuning*	
128,4634 Hz	128,8994 Hz	← C
136,1022 Hz	136,5642 Hz	← C#
144,1953 Hz	144,6847 Hz	← D
152,7696 Hz	153,2881 Hz	← D#
161,8537 Hz	162,4031 Hz	← E
171,4780 Hz	172,0601 Hz	← F
181,6747 Hz	182,2913 Hz	← F#
192,4776 Hz	193,1309 Hz	← G
203,9229 Hz	204,6151 Hz	← G#
216,0488 Hz	216,7821 Hz	← A
228,8957 Hz	229,6726 Hz	← A#
242,5066 Hz	243,3297 Hz	← H (B)
256,9268 Hz	257,7988 Hz	← C
272,2044 Hz	273,1283 Hz	← C#
288,3905 Hz	289,3694 Hz	← D
305,5391 Hz	306,5762 Hz	← D#
323,7074 Hz	324,8062 Hz	← E
342,9561 Hz	344,1202 Hz	← F
363,3493 Hz	364,5826 Hz	← F#
384,9552 Hz	386,2618 Hz	← G
407,8458 Hz	409,2301 Hz	← G#
432,0976 Hz	433,5642 Hz	← A
457,7914 Hz	459,3453 Hz	← A#
485,0131 Hz	486,6594 Hz	← H (B)
513,8535 Hz	515,5977 Hz	← C

$$\frac{1}{31\ 556\ 925{,}97 \ \text{sec}} \cdot 2^{32}$$

$$= 136{,}1022 \ \text{Hz}$$

$$\frac{2^{47}}{31\ 556\ 926 \cdot 25\ 920 \ \text{sec}}$$

$$= 172{,}060\ 1 \ \text{Hz}$$

THE MULTIPLICATION FACTORS
OF THE FREQUENCIES OF THE INTERVALS

*The calculation from chromatic to diatonic
and from diatonic to chromatic*

name of interval	diatonic — lenght of vibrating part of a string	diatonic — relation of frequencies	chromatic — relation of frequencies
basic note	1/1 →	1/1 = 1,000 000	$\sqrt[12]{2^0}$ = 1,000 000
minor second	15/16 →	15/16 = 1,066 667	$\sqrt[12]{2^1}$ = 1,059 463
major second	8/9 → 9/10 →	9/8 = 1,125 000 10/9 = 1,111 111	$\sqrt[12]{2^2}$ = 1,122 462 $\sqrt[12]{2^2}$ = 1,122 462
minor third	5/6 →	6/5 = 1,200 000	$\sqrt[12]{2^3}$ = 1,189 207
major third	4/5 →	5/4 = 1,250 000	$\sqrt[12]{2^4}$ = 1,259 921
fourth	3/4 →	4/3 = 1,333 333	$\sqrt[12]{2^5}$ = 1,334 840
tritone	32/45 →	45/32 = 1,406 250	$\sqrt[12]{2^6}$ = 1,414 214
fifth	2/3 →	3/2 = 1,500 000	$\sqrt[12]{2^7}$ = 1,498 307
minor sixth	5/8 →	8/5 = 1,600 000	$\sqrt[12]{2^8}$ = 1,587 401
major sixth	3/5 →	5/3 = 1,666 667	$\sqrt[12]{2^9}$ = 1,681 793
minor seventh	5/9 →	9/5 = 1,800 000	$\sqrt[12]{2^{10}}$ = 1,781 797
major seventh	8/15 →	15/8 = 1,875 000	$\sqrt[12]{2^{11}}$ = 1,887 749
octave	1/2 →	2 = 2,000 000	$\sqrt[12]{2^{12}}$ = 2,000 000
octave+fifth	1/3 →	3 = 3,000 000	$\sqrt[12]{2^{19}}$ = 2,996 614

Table of Periods and Frequencies

Planet Name	Symb.	period (u) in days	(f₁) in Hz	(n) number of octave	name of tone	corresponding tuning pitch A' in Hz	(f₂) in Hz · 10¹⁴	(p) number of octave	wavelength (λ) in micrometer	Color
			audible frequency				visible frequency			
Mercury	☿	87,9690	141,27	30	d	423,34	6,213	72	0,483	blue
Venus	♀	224,7008	221,23	32	a	442,46	4,865	73	0,616	orange
Earth	♁	1 Jahr Tropisch	136,10	32	c$^\sharp$	432,10	5,986	74	0,501	blue-green
Mars	♂	686,9798 (ca. 2 Jahre)	144,72	33	d	433,67	6,365	75	0,471	blue
Jupiter	♃	4332,588 (ca. 12 Jahre)	183,58	36	f$^\sharp$	436,62	4,037	77	0,743	red
Saturn	♄	10759,21 (ca. 30 Jahre)	147,85	37	d	443,04	6,502	79	0,461	blue
Uranus	♅	30689,6 (ca. 84 Jahre)	207,33	39	g$^\sharp$	439,32	4,559	80	0,685	orange-red
Neptune	♆	60183,6 (ca. 165 Jahre)	211,45	40	a	422,90	4,650	81	0,645	orange-red
Pluto	♇	90740,5 (ca. 248 Jahre)	140,25	40	c$^\sharp$	445,25	6,168	82	0,486	blue
Moon Syn.	☽	29,530588	210,42	29·	g$^\sharp$	445,86	4,627	70	0,648	orange-red
Moon Sid.	☽	27.321661	227,43	29	a$^\sharp$	429,33	5,001	70	0,599	yellow-orange
day average		1 Tag = 24 h	194,18	24	g	435,92	4,270	65	0,702	orange-red
Tag day Sid. sid		0,99726957 = 23h56'4,091"	194,71	24	g	437,11	4,282	65	0,700	orange-red
Platonic year		25920 Jahre	344,12	48	f	433,56	7,567	89	0,396	red-violet

RHYTHMEN DER PLANETEN, DER ERDE UND DES MONDES.
RHYTHMUS OF THE PLANETS, OF THE EARTH AND OF THE MOON.

Planet		period		Number of octaves (n)	period in minutes	beats per minutes in the		
Name	Symbol	in days	in minutes			(n)th octave	(n+1)st octave	(n+2)nd octave
Mercury	☿	87,9690	126 675,36′	22	0,030 2017′	33,11	62,22	132,44
Venus	♀	224,7008	323 569,15′	24	0,019 2862′	51,85	103,70	207,40
Earth	⊕	(1 trop. Jahr)	525 948,77′	24	525 948,77′	31,90	63,80	127,60
Mars	♂	686,9798	989 250,91′	25	0,029 4820′	33,92	67,84	135,68
Jupiter	♃	4 332,588	6 238 926,72′	28	0,023 2418′	43,03	86,05	172,10
Saturn	♄	10 759,21	15 493 262,4′	29	0,028 8585′	34,65	69,30	138,61
Uranus	♅	30 689,6	44 193 024′	31	0,020 5789′	48,59	97,19	194,37
Neptune	♆	60 138,6	86 599 584′	32	0,020 1630′	49,60	99,19	198,38
Pluto	♇	90 740,5	130 666 320′	32	0.030 4231′	32,87	65,74	131,49
Moon	☽ Syn.	29,530 588	42 524,047′	21	0,020 2770′	49,32	98,63	197,27
	☽ Sid.	27,321 661	39 343,192′	21	0,018 7603′	53,30	106,61	213,22
day	mittlerer average day	24h. = 1 d.	1440′	16	0,021 9727′	45,51	91,02	182,04
	sid. day	23h 56′ 4,091″ = 0,997 2696 d	1436,068′	16	0,021 9127′	45,64	91,27	182,54
latonic year		25 920 Jahre	1,363 259 10¹⁰′	39	0,024 7975′	40,33	80,65	161,31

ILLUSTRATIONS AND ANNOTATIONS
TO THE TABLE
OF PERIODS AND FREQUENCIES

The period for ☽ (sid. and syn.), ☿, ♀, ♂, ♃ have
been taken from: »Rhythmen der Sterne«, by
J. Schulz, ed. by the Mathematical-Astronomical
Section of the Goetheanum, Dornach/CH, ed. 1977.
The periods for ♄, ♅, ♆ and ♇ have been taken
from: »Musik und Kosmos als Schöpfungswunder«,
by Thomas M. Schmidt, Frankfurt a.M., ed. 1974,
(published by the author).
The duration of the tropical earth year was fixed in
1957 and serves as a unit of measurement for the so-
called sidereal time. According to that, a tropical year
has the duration of 31 556 925.974 7 seconds.
(»Kalender für Sternenfreunde«, by Paul Ahnert,
Sternwarte Sonnenberg, DDR, Johann Ambrosius
Barth Verlag, Leipzig.)
For the planet Pluto, still difficult to observe, even
today various times of revolution are given in the different reference books, differing by several days. Pluto
was discovered as late as 1930, Neptune in 1846,
and Uranus in 1781.

From the period (u) the reciprocal value ($\frac{1}{u}$) is formed. This, multiplied with n octaves, yields the given
frequency in the audible range: ($f_t = \frac{1}{u} \cdot 2^n$).
Then the chromatic note (based on an A' of 435
Hertz) which lies closest to this frequency is located.
This note lies within the frequency range between
($f_t : \sqrt[24]{2}$) and ($f_t \cdot \sqrt[24]{2}$) and is given as the name
of the note.

From the note thus ascertained the semitones to A'
are counted. When there are m semitones, the chromatic A' which is correlated to (f_t) can be calculated
with the formula ($f_t \cdot \sqrt[12]{2^m}$). Electronic tuning
machines with a frequency indicator for the note A'
can then be attuned accordingly.

The corresponding frequency of light in the visible
range is attained by multiplying the reciprocal value
($\frac{1}{u}$) of the period (u) with p octaves according to the
formula ($\frac{1}{u} \cdot 2^p$). The formula for the frequency in the
visible range is therefore ($f_s = \frac{1}{u} \cdot 2^p$).

The wave-length (λ) is calculated from the equation
($\lambda = \frac{c}{f}$), where by c (c = 2.997 925 micrometer/-
second $\cdot 10^{14}$) = the speed of light.
(299 792.5 km/sec. = 2.997 925 $\cdot 10^{14}$ μm/sec.)

THE SECOND APPENDIX

KEPLER'S THIRD LAW AND GRAVITATION

The first law discovered by Kepler states: the planets move in elliptical paths with the sun located at one focus of the ellipse. The second law states that a line drawn between a planet and the sun, also called the radius vector, sweeps over equal areas in equal time intervals. The third law states that the square of the planet's orbital period u is proportional to the cube of its average distance from the sun a. Assume that the orbital period of one planet is u1 and the period of a second planet is u2, and that their average distances from the sun are a1 and a2, respectively, then the following equation holds true:

$$P = (u1)^2 \cdot (a1)^{-3} = (u2)^2 \cdot (a2)^{-3} \tag{I}$$

where P is a constant. Based on Kepler's second law, Newton was able to prove that planetary motion in elliptical paths by holding to Kepler's law of areas leads to the $1/r^2$ law, and that conversely, the inverse-square law always gives orbital paths which are conic sections (an ellipse is a conic section) with the central mass at one focus. The gravitational force between two masses is given by:

$$K = \gamma \cdot (m1) \cdot (m2) \cdot (r)^{-2} \tag{II}$$

where m1 and m2 are the two masses attracting each other, r is the distance between the centers of gravity of the masses, and γ is the gravitational constant.

$$\gamma = 6.6740 \cdot 10^{-8} \, cm^3 \cdot g^{-1} \cdot sec^{-2}$$

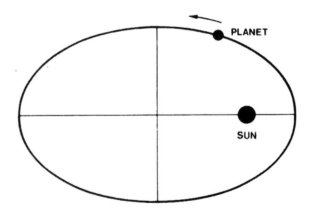

Kepler's first law states that the planets move in elliptical paths about the sun, with the sun located at one focus of the ellipse.

Kepler's third law, taking Newton's theory of gravity into account, then becomes:

$$P = (M + m1) \cdot (u1)^2 \cdot (a1)^{-3} = (M + m2) \cdot (u2)^2 \cdot (a2)^{-3} \quad \text{(III)}$$

where u1 is the orbital period of the first planet, a1 is its average distance from the sun and m1 is its mass, and u2, a2 and m2 are the corresponding values for the second planet. M is the mass of the sun.

Astronomical yearbooks usually list not only the orbital period of a planet, but also its mean daily motion n. The conversion of orbital period u to mean daily motion n is given by:

$$u^{-1} \cdot 360° = n \quad \text{(IV)}; \qquad \text{or} \qquad n^{-1} \cdot 360° = u \quad \text{(V)}$$

By taking the force of gravity into account and substituting equation (IV) for the mean daily motion in equation (III), Kepler's third law can be rewritten as:

$$a^3 \cdot n^2 = k^2 \cdot (1 + m) \quad \text{(VI)}$$

where a is the average distance of the planet from the sun measured in astronomical units (AU), n is the mean daily motion in degrees of arc, m is the mass of the planet in solar mass units, and k is a constant, the so-called Gaussian gravitational constant, which expressed in degrees of arc is 0.985 607 668 6. The exact value in seconds of arc is 3 548.187 606 965 1 seconds. The first column of the table on page 115 lists the average distances from the sun of the planets Mercury to Saturn, with the value a given in astronomical units (AU). The planets Mercury to Saturn are those which

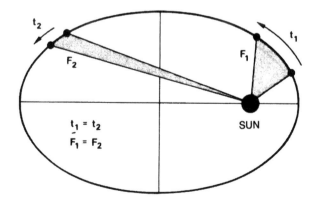

Kepler's second law states that a line drawn between a planet and the sun, also called the radius vector, sweeps over equal areas in equal time intervals. t is a time interval of specified length, F is the area swept out in this time interval.

Planet	(a)	(n)	(m)	$a^3 \cdot n^2$	(k)
Mercury	0.387 10	4.092 34	$1.59 \cdot 10^{-7}$	0.971 4	0.985 6
Venus	0.723 33	1.602 13	$2.45 \cdot 10^{-6}$	0.971 4	0.985 6
Earth	1.000 00	0.985 61	$3.00 \cdot 10^{-6}$	0.971 4	0.985 6
Mars	1.526 9	0.524 03	$3.22 \cdot 10^{-7}$	0.971 4	0.985 6
Jupiter	5.202 80	0.083 09	$9.56 \cdot 10^{-4}$	0.972 3	0.985 6
Saturn	9.538 84	0.033 46	$2.86 \cdot 10^{-4}$	0.971 7	0.985 6

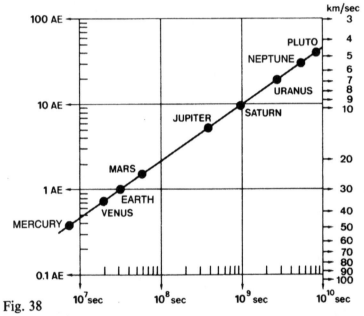

Fig. 38

Kepler's Third Law of Planetary Motion (above).

The above illustration demonstrates Kepler's third law of planetary motion and the law of gravity. Below: a graph of the solar system on log-log paper.[37]

At the top is a table illustrating Kepler's third law and gravitation. The table is discussed on pages 112 to 114. At the bottom is a double logarithmic plot representing the solar system. It is discussed at the top of page 116.

were known in Kepler's time and can be seen without a telescope. The second column lists the mean daily motion n in degrees of arc; the third column the masses of the planets in solar mass units; the fourth column lists the values of the expression $(a^3 \cdot n^2)$; and the fifth column shows the value of k for each planet. As the table shows, the expression in the fourth column is not constant but deviates from the mean for the planets Jupiter and Saturn. This is due to the relatively large masses of these two planets. Since these values were calculated with:

$$a^3 \cdot n^2 = k^2 \cdot (1 + m)$$

we must divide $a^3 \cdot n^2$ by $1 + m$ to arrive at a constant value. The value of k^2, and k, is then a constant. The value k is generally known as the Gaussian gravitational constant, as mentioned above.

The average orbital speed v of the planets is calculated with the equation:

$$v = 2 \cdot \pi \cdot a \cdot u^{-1} \text{ with the units being AU} \cdot d^{-1} \qquad \text{(VII)}$$

where $AU \cdot d^{-1}$ is astronomical units per day. Expressed in terms of the mean daily motion by substituting equation (V) in equation (VII) , this equation becomes:

$$v = 2 \cdot \pi \cdot a \cdot n \cdot (360°)^{-1} \text{ AU} \cdot d^{-1} \qquad \text{(VIII)}$$

$$v = a \cdot n \cdot \pi \cdot (180°)^{-1} \text{ AU} \cdot d^{-1} \qquad \text{(IX)}$$

If we multiply this value by the numer of kilometers represented by one AU, 149 587 870 kilometers, then we obtain the orbital speed in km per day; if we then divide the result by the average number of seconds in a day (calendar day), which

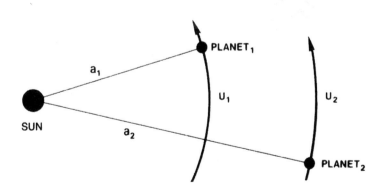

Kepler's third law states that the squares of the orbital period u of the planets are proportional to the cubes of their average distance from the sun a.

When substituting the numerical values in this equation, we must make sure that the units agree; v must be given in astronomical units per day since n is the mean daily motion and the constant k has been calculated for astronomical units; therefore, we must divide the speed of light, $2.997925 \cdot 10^{10}$ cm/sec, by the astronomical unit in centimeters, $1.49597870 \cdot 10^{13}$, and then multiply the result by 86,400 (the number of seconds per day).

$$v = 2.997\,925 \cdot 10^{10} \text{cm} \cdot \text{sec}^{-1}$$

$$= 2.003\,989 \cdot 10^{-3} \text{AU} \cdot \text{sec}^{-1} = 173.144\,658\ \text{AU} \cdot \text{d}^{-1}$$

The numerical values with corresponding units can now be substituted in equation (XIII):

$$a =$$
$$0.985\,607\,668\,6^2 \cdot 3.141\,592\,654^2 \cdot 173.144\,658^{-2} \cdot 180^{-2} \cdot 1\ \text{AU}$$

$$a = 9.870\,625\,8 \cdot 10^{-9} \text{AU} =$$

$$1.476\,624\,6\ \text{km} = 1\,476.624\,6\ \text{m} = 1.476\,624\,6 \cdot 10^5 \text{cm}$$

According to equation (VI) the following relationship holds:

$$n^2 = k^2 \cdot a^{-3} \quad \text{(VIa)} \qquad \text{and therefore, } n = k \cdot a^{-1.5} \qquad \text{(VIb)}$$

If we now insert the values for k and a (from equation XIV) into equation (VIb), we can calculate the mean daily motion:

$$n = 0.985\,607\,668\,6 \cdot (9.870\,625\,8 \cdot 10^{-9} \text{AU})^{-1.5}$$

$$n = 1.005\,048\,5 \cdot 10^{12}$$

This corresponds to an orbital period of:

$$u = n^{-1} \cdot 360° = 3.581\,916\,5 \cdot 10^{-10} \text{days} = 3.094\,775\,9 \cdot 10^{-5} \text{ seconds}$$

or a frequency of:

$$f = u^{-1} = 32\,312.52\ \text{Hz}$$

This shows that for our hypothetical point-sized planet, which orbits around a point-sized sun, a minimum distance from the sun of approximately 1.5 km results. This is valid at least for our solar system, or for any sun with the same mass as our sun. This minimum distance is referred to in physics and astronomy as the gravitational length (R_0). The method shown above for deriving its value is not the method commonly used (which will be discussed briefly below), but has the advantage that it does not require a knowledge of the theory of relativity, and that the physical principles involved can be easily followed by the layman without his having to have a university education in physics or astronomy.

   Albert Einstein, who developed the theory of relativity, arrived at the following, well known, equation:

$$E = m \cdot c^2$$

is 86 400, we obtain the orbital speed in km · sec^{-1}. The factor for converting AU · d^{-1} to km · sec^{-1} is thus

$$1.495\,978\,70 \cdot 10^8 \cdot 86\,400^{-1} = 1{,}731.4568 \tag{X}$$

The figure on page 115 shows a double logarithmic plot representing the solar system. The x-axis is the orbital periods of the planets in seconds, the left y-axis is the average distance of the planets from the sun (in astronomical units), and the right y-axis shows the orbital speed in kilometers per second. If we draw a line through all of the planets in this system, we discover that they lie on a straight line. This double logarithmic plot of the planets' distances from the sun, their orbital periods, and their orbital speeds very clearly illustrates the inherent cosmic order of the solar system. Of course, this order applies not only to our solar system, but to every other similar system.

The Gravitational Length of the Sun and Black Holes

Consider a hypothetical planet as a single point moving at the speed of light in an orbit about a sun, also a point (actually we must say *almost* at the speed of light, but let us assume that the planet's speed is only slightly less than the speed of light). Further assume that the imaginary planet has a very small mass so that it becomes negligible compared to the mass of the sun. As shown in the previous section, the following relationships apply:

$$v = a \cdot n \cdot \pi \cdot (180°)^{-1} \text{ in units of AU} \cdot d^{-1} \tag{IX}$$

and

$$a^3 \cdot n^2 = k^2 \cdot (1+m) \tag{VI}$$

The following quantities are known in these two equations:

$v = 2.997\,925 \cdot 10^{10}$ cm·sec^{-1}; $k = 0.985\,607\,668\,6$ deg; $\pi = 3.141\,592\,65...$

and m, which is negligibly small, i. e., it will be assumed that m = 0, or it will be left out of the equation, e. g., (1 + m) = 1. We wish to find a, the average distance from the center of gravity of the sun, and n, the mean daily motion. Solving equation (IX) for n gives:

$$n = v \cdot (180°) \cdot a^{-1} \cdot \pi^{-1} \tag{XI}$$

Substituting equation (XI) in equation (VI) and letting m lim → 0 gives:

$$a^3 \cdot v^2 \cdot (180°)^2 \cdot a^{-2} \cdot \pi^{-2} = k^2 \tag{XII}$$
$$= a \cdot a^2 \cdot v^2 \cdot (180°)^2 \cdot a^{-2} \cdot \pi^{-2} = k^2$$

In this equation, a^2 can be cancelled and the equation can be solved for a with the result:

$$a = k^2 \cdot \pi^2 \cdot v^{-2} \cdot (180°)^{-2} \tag{XIII}$$

This equation states that the energy E is equal to the mass m times the square of the speed of light (the speed of light is represented by c). It suggests itself to calculate the gravitational length by setting the gravitational energy of a body equal to $m \cdot c^2$:

$$\gamma \cdot m^2 \cdot (R_o)^{-1} = m \cdot c^2 \qquad \text{(XV)}$$

$$R_o = \gamma \cdot m \cdot c^{-2} \qquad \text{(XVa)}$$

where $\gamma = 6.6740 \cdot 10^{-8}$ $cm^3 \cdot g^{-1} \cdot sec^{-2}$ is the gravitational constant, m is the mass of the body, in our case the mass of the sun with $m = 1.989 \cdot 10^{33}$ g, and $c = 2.997\,925 \cdot 10^{10}$ $cm \cdot sec^{-1}$. R_o is the gravitational length of the sun, which we wish to find. By simply substituting the numerical values in equation (XV) or equation (XVa), we obtain:

$R_o =$
$6.6740 \cdot 10^{-8} cm^3 \cdot g^{-1} \cdot sec^{-2} \cdot 1.989 \cdot 10^{33} g \cdot (2.997\,925 \cdot 10^{10} cm \cdot sec^{-1})^{-2}$

$R_o = 1.476\,996 \cdot 10^5 cm$ = approximately 1.477 kilometers.

We recognize immediately that this value agrees with the average distance a calculated previously for our hypothetical planet. The devitation of the values after the fourth significant digit is due to the fact that the mass of the sun and the gravitational constant are known with certainty at present to only four significant digits. It follows from the general theory of relativity that the gravitational length R_o is of fundamental importance. It appears that light rays (photons) cannot escape from the surface of bodies with a large mass whose radius R is less than or equal to the gravitational length R_o. Such bodies absorb all light falling on them and cannot themselves emit light. These bodies are therefore called black holes.

Bibliography

Some of the important articles and books used as reference material in this book were not availible in English; others were hard to find. Also, the process of listing and ordering books is different in each country. We have, therefore, printed all the information we could gather about the following titles, with an apology where we are incomplete.

Asimova, Isaac. *The Black Hole.* Francis Reddy, 1994.

Baker, Jeannine Parvati. *Conscious Conception.* Berkeley, North Atlantic Books, 1986.

Berendt, Joachim E. *Nada Brahma; The World Is Sound.* New York: Inner Tradition, 1987.

Cousto, Hans. *Farbton - Tonfarbe, und die Kosmische Oktave Band II.* Mainz: Selbstverlag, 1982.

Danielou, Alain. *Einführung in die indische Musik.* Taschenbuch zur Musikwissenschaft, Heinrichshofen, 1975.

Downing, George. *Massage and Meditation.* New York: Random House, 1974.

Evans-Wentz, W.Y. *The Tibeten Book of the Dead.* New York: Oxford University Press. 3rd ed. 1957.

Gebser, Jean. *The Ever-Present Origin.* Athens, Ohio: Ohio University Pess, 1986.

Grof, Stanislav. *The Adventure of Self-Discovery: Dimension of Consciousness and New Perspective in Psychotherapy and Inner Exploration.* Albany, New York: SUNY Press, 1987.

Grof, Stanislav. *Beyond the Brain; Birth, Death and Transcendence in Psychotherapy.* Albany, New York: SUNY Press, 1985.

Grof, Stanislav, ed. *Ancient Wisdom and Modern Science.* Mill Valley, CA: Rob Briggs Associates, 1985.

Grof, Stanislav and Marjorie L. Valier, Eds. *Human Survival and Consciousness Evolution.* Albany, New York: SUNY, 1987.

Hesse, Hermann. *Magister Ludi: The Glass Bead Game.* New York: Bantam Books, 1970.

Hofmann, Albert. *LSD My Problem Child; Reflection on Sacred Drugs, Mysticism and Science.* 1983.

Huxley, Aldous. *Brave New World.* New York: Harper and Row, 1932.

Huxley, Aldous. *Island.* New York: Harper and Row, 1972.

Huxley, Aldous. *The Doors of Perception.* New York: Harper and Row, 1970.

Inayat Kahn, Hazrat. *Music.* San Bernadino, CA: Borgo Press, 1985.

Kayser, Hans. *Akroasis; The Theory of World Harmonics.* Boston: Plowshare Press, 1970.

Kepler, Johannes. *Mysterium Cosmographicom.* tr. A. M. Duncan, New York: Abaris Books, 1977.

Kepler, Johannes. *Somnium; The Dream of Posthumous Work on Lunar Astronomy.* Edward Rosen, tr. Ann Arbor, Michigan, Books on Demand, 1965.

Lao Tzu. *Way of Life; Tao Te Ching.* New York. NAL Penguin Inc. 1955.

Leary. Timothy. *Exo-Psychology.* Phoenix, AZ: Falcon Press, 1987.

Leary. Timothy. *Flashbacks: An Autobiography.* Los Angeles: J. P. tarcher, 1984.

Leary. Timothy. *Neuropolitics.* Phoenix, Arizona: Falcon Press, 1987.

Lilly, John. *The Center of the Cyclon; an Autobiography of Inner Space.* New York: Crown Publishers, 1985.

Lilly, John. *The Deep Self.* New York: Warner Books, 1978.

Lilly, John. *Programming & Mataprogramming in the Human Biocomputer.* New York: Crown Publisher, 1987.

Orr, Leonard and Sondra Ray. *Rebirthing in the New Age.* Berkeley Celestial Arts, 1978.

Ram Dass. *Be Here Now.* New York: Crown Publishers, 1971.

Rosenberg, Jack Lee. *Orgasm.* New York: Random House, 1973.

Sheldrake, Rupert. *New Science of Life; Hypothesis of Formative Causation,* J. Tarcher, 1981.

Shankar, Ravi. *Meine Musik, mein Leben.* München: Nymphenburger Velagsanstalt, 1969.

Thimus, Albert von. *Die harmonikale Symbolik des Altertums.* Köln: M. Dumont Schauberg, 1968.

Townsend, Larry. *The Leatherman's Handbook II.* New York: Modernismo, 1983.

Watts, Alan. *The Book: On the Taboo Against Knowing Who You Are.* New York: Random House, 1972.

Watts, Alan. *The Supreme Identity.* New York: Random House, 1972.

Watts, Alan. *Wisdom of Insecurity.* New York: Random House, 1968.

Acknowledgements

The Following illustrations were drawn especially for this book by Chris Stone, in close collaboration with the author: 1, 2, 5, 6, 4, 7, 8, 9, 13, 14, 15.

The following illustrations were taken from *Relating Sound to Color and the Cosmic Octave*, vol. I: 29, 30.

The following illustrations were taken from *Farbton – Tonfarb und die Kosmische Oktave*: 11, 21, 23.

The following illustrations were taken from *Die Kosmische Oktave*: 22, 26, 27, 34, 35.

The following illustration was taken from *Tantra, Weg der Ekstase*: 16.

The following illustrations are based on the acupuncture tables published by Plejaden Verlag: 17, 18, 19, 20, 24, 25, 31, 32, 33.

Figure 10 was taken from the *Technischer Informationsdienst*.

LifeRhythm Publications

John C. Pierrakos M.D   CORE ENERGETICS
Developing the Capacity to Love and Heal
With 16 pages of four-color illustrations of human auras corresponding to their character structure, 300 pages
John C. Pierrakos, M.D., is a psychiatrist, body-therapist and an authority on consciousness and human energy fields. The focus of his work is to open the "Core" of his patients to a new awareness of how body, emotions, mind , will and spirituality form a unit. Dr. Pierrakos is considered one of the founders of a whole new movement in therapeutic work, integrating body, mind and spirit and this book has become classic.

John C. Pierrakos M.D.   EROS, LOVE & SEXUALITY
The Unifying Forces of Life and Relationship
150 pages
The free flow of the three great forces of life—eros, love and sexuality—is our greatest source of pleasure. These three forces are simply different aspects of the life force, and when we stay open, they are experienced as one. They generate all activity, all creativity. This book has been long awaited. John Pierrakos, the great psychiatrist, was a student and colleague of Wilhelm Reich, and co-founder of Bioenergetics; he later developed his own therapeutic work, Core Energetics, which integrates the higher dimensions into our physical existence.

Malcolm Brown, Ph.D.   THE HEALING TOUCH
An Introduction to Organismic Psychotherapy
320 pages 38 illustrations
A moving and meticulous account of Malcolm Brown's journey from Rogerian-style verbal psychotherapist to gifted body psychotherapist. Dr. Brown developed his own art and science of body psychotherapy with the purpose of re-activating the natural mental/spiritual polarities of the embodied soul and transcendental psyche. Using powerful case histories as examples, Brown describes in theory and practice the development of his work; the techniques to awaken the energy flow and its integration with the main Being centers: Eros, Logos, the Spritual Warrior and the Hara.

Anna Halprin   RETURNING TO HEALTH
With Dance, Movement & Imagery
195 pages illustrations
In this graceful book Anna Halprin offers the wisdom of her life experience as a dancer, teacher and healer. As a cancer survivor, she tells her own story and that of many others with deep compassion and uplifting clarity. Originally written as a manual for teachers, this book is filled with guidance and insights into the emotional processes of a health crises and well as clear guidelines for leading groups and classes in healing movement.

Helmut G. Sieczka   CHAKRA BREATHING
A Pathway to Energy and Harmony
100 pages Illustrations   Supplemental Cassette Tape of Guided Meditations
A guide to self-healing, this book is meant to help activate and harmonize the energy centers of the subtle body. The breath is the bridge between body and soul. In today's world as our lives are determined by stressful careers and peak performance, the silent and meditative moments have become more vital. Remembering our true selves, our natural energy balances are restored. Chakra-breathing enhances this kind of awareness and transformational work, especially on the emotional and energetic level.

R. Stamboliev   THE ENERGETICS OF
VOICE DIALOGUE
Exploring the Energetics of Transformational Psychology
100 pages
Voice Dialogue is a therapeutic technique based on the transformational model of consciousness. This book approaches the human psyche as a synthesis of experience-patterns which may be modified only when the original pattern of an experience has been touched, understood and felt from an adult, integrated perspective, developing an "Aware Ego".   This book explores the energetic aspects of the relationship between client and therapist, offering exercises for developing energetic skills and giving case histories to illustrate these skills. Voice Dialogue is the work of Hal and Sidra Stone Ph.Ds.

Fran Brown   LIVING REIKI: TAKATA'S TEACHINGS
Stories from the Life of Hawayo Takata
110 pages
In this loving memoir to her teacher, Fran Brown has gathered the colorful stories told by Hawayo Takata during her thirty-five years s the only Reiki Master Teaching. The stories create an inspirational panorama of Takata's teachings, filled with the practical and spiritual aspects of a life given to healing.

Müller&Günther A COMPLETE BOOK OF
REIKI HEALING
Heal Yourself, Others, and the World Around You
192 pages, 85 photographs and illustrations
This book includes the history and practice of Reiki, with photographs and drawings as well as clear instructions for placement of hands in giving Reiki. Brigitte Müller was the first Reiki Master in Europe and she writes about her opening into a new world of healing with the freshness of discovery. Horst Günther experienced Reiki at one of Brigitte's first workshops in Germany, and it changed the course of his life. They share a vision of Reiki and the use of universal life energy to help us all heal ourselves and our world.

Bodo Baginski & Shalila Sharamon   REIKI Universal Life Energy
200 pages illustrations
This is the first book ever written about Reiki. Reiki is described as the energy which forms the basis of all life. With the help of specific methods, anyone can learn to awaken and activate this universal life energy so that healing and harmonizing energy flows through the hands. Reiki is healing energy in the truest sense of the word, leading to greater individual harmony and attunement to the basic forces of the universe. This book features a unique compilation and interpretation, from the author's experience, of over 200 psychosomatic symptoms and diseases